CHALLENGER 8

ADULT READING SERIES

NEW READERS PRESS
Publishing Division of Laubach Literacy International
Syracuse, New York

Every effort has been made to locate the persons or agencies authorized to give permission to reprint the selection from *The Shape of Futures Past* by Chris Morgan found in Lesson 9 and *The Man Who Invented Baseball* by Harold Peterson found in Lesson 19. If these persons or agencies are located subsequent to publication, they are hereby entitled to due compensation.

ISBN 0-88336-788-2

New Readers Press
Publishing Division of Laubach Literacy International
Box 131, Syracuse, New York 13210

Printed in the United States of America

Designed by Chris Steenwerth
Cover by Chris Steenwerth

Cover photo by Royce Bair & Associates

9 8 7 6 5 4 5 3 2

About the Author

Corea Murphy has worked in the field of education since the early 1960s. Currently she teaches reading and English at Lincoln Hall, a school for adolescent boys in Lincolndale, New York. In addition to classroom and tutorial teaching, Ms. Murphy has developed language arts curriculum guides for public high schools, conducted curriculum and effectiveness workshops, and established an educational program for residents in a drug rehabilitation facility.

Ms. Murphy became interested in creating a reading series for older students when she began working with illiterate adults and adolescents in the early 1970s. The **Challenger Adult Reading Series** is the result of her work with these students.

In a very real sense, these students contributed greatly to the development of this reading series. Their enthusiasm for learning to read and their willingness to work hard provided inspiration, and their many helpful suggestions influenced the content of both the student books and the teacher's manual.

It is to these students that the **Challenger Adult Reading Series** is dedicated with the hope that others who wish to become good readers will find this reading program both helpful and stimulating.

Table of Contents

Unit 1

Appearances

The theme of this unit—*appearances*—is a very interesting and complex concept. One meaning of *appearance* deals with the way people look—the images they project. These images deliver messages, telling other people something about themselves. Another meaning of *appearance* suggests deception or giving a false impression. Used in this sense, *appearance* implies an illusion, a contrast between what something seems to be and what it really is.

The reading for Lesson 1 deals with appearance as deception or illusion. In this selection, "Houdini: His Legend and His Magic," you will read about one of the most famous magicians of all times—Harry Houdini.

The reading for Lesson 2, "Mirror, Mirror on the Wall...," examines the notion of personal appearance. In this selection, you will learn how, throughout the ages, people have used cosmetics and other forms of body art to deliver messages about themselves.

The reading for Lesson 3 is entitled "Television: The Image-Maker." In this selection, the author presents his views about how television often misrepresents reality and the dangers resulting from these misrepresentations.

Most of us have heard the expression, "Keeping up with the Joneses," the title of the reading for Lesson 4. This reading, taken from a book which was written at the end of the last century, explores how people go about trying to appear wealthy and powerful. As you study the ideas in this reading, it will be helpful to consider whether or not the author's ideas about the time and money people spend creating the appearance of wealth and power still hold true today.

The reading for Lesson 5 is a short story by the American author O. Henry. In this story, titled "While the Auto Waits," you will see what happens when two characters decide that deception is more interesting than reality.

Lesson 1

Houdini: His Legend and His Magic

Words for Study

Houdini	illusion	Americanization	sustain
extrication	chloroform	exhibition	rupture
feat	dismember	shackles	neutrality
Hungary	memoirs	publicize	disentangle

Houdini: His Legend and His Magic

In the year 1920, Harry Houdini, then at the peak of his career, was justly proud that his name had become an accepted part of the English language. That year's edition of *Funk and Wagnall's New Standard Dictionary* carried the following entry:

> Hou di-ni, Harry (4/6 1874-) American mystericist, wizard and expert in extrication and self release,—hou di-nize, vb. To release or extricate oneself from (confinement, bonds, or the like), as by wriggling out.

The verb *to houdinize* has hardly found its way into standard usage, but the name of Houdini has become part of the vocabulary not only of American culture, but of cultures throughout the world. If we say a person is a *Houdini*, what we mean is immediately understood. That Houdini escaped from handcuffs, packing boxes and straitjackets; that he made an elephant disappear on the stage of the world's largest theater; that he could swallow needles and thread and bring the needles up threaded; that at one point in his career he performed the astonishing feat of walking through a brick wall—these are all parts of the legend. And today, to be a Houdini is to be able to do the seemingly impossible.

Houdini's origins have, until very recently, been shrouded in mystery. One reason for this

The Bettman Archive

mystery is that both Houdini and members of his family gave false information to the public. In hundreds of interviews with the press, for example, Houdini always gave his date of birth as April 6, 1874, and his birthplace as Appleton, Wisconsin. Yet careful research has revealed that Houdini's true date and place of birth were March 24, 1874, in Budapest, Hungary.

Houdini's real name was Ehrich Weiss, and he is said to have been the son of a Hungarian rabbi. When he was still an infant, his family moved to the United States and settled in Milwaukee, Wisconsin. Houdini comments on those years in Milwaukee as a time when "such hardships and hunger became our lot; the less said on the subject the better."

It was during the years in Milwaukee that Ehrich Weiss was first exposed to magic. Most professional magicians become fascinated with magic by seeing and being astonished by another magician, and Houdini was no exception. It is likely that this happened when Rabbi Weiss took his son to a stage performance of a traveling magician named Dr. Lynn.

Dr. Lynn's magic act featured an illusion in which he pretended to give chloroform to a man and then, after tying him in place inside a cabinet, proceeded to dismember the man with a huge butcher knife, cutting off his legs and arms and finally his head. The pieces were then thrown into the cabinet and the curtain was pulled. Moments later, the victim appeared from the cabinet restored to one living piece, and seemingly none the worst for the ordeal. Many years later Houdini purchased this illusion (reportedly for $75) from Dr. Lynn's son and presented it without the chloroform during the last two years of his show.

In 1888, Rabbi Weiss moved his family to New York City. Ehrich had run away from home on his twelfth birthday in an attempt to find work and help support the family, but he joined them at their new house on East 69th Street and found employment as a cutter in a necktie factory. It was during this period that Ehrich became seriously interested in the art of magic. One of the books he was reading at the time was *The Memoirs of Robert-Houdin*, the biography of the great French magician who is generally considered to be "the father of modern magic."

Ehrich told a friend of his desire to be as great as Robert-Houdin, and his friend suggested that if he added the letter *i* to Houdin's name, it would mean "like Houdin," and he could call himself Houdini. This, with the Americanization of his nickname, Ehrie, into Harry, produced the name that was, forever after, to mean *magic*—Harry Houdini.

In 1891, Harry Houdini left his job at the necktie factory and made the plunge into a career as a professional magician. He barely managed, and by 1893, he was doing as many as twenty shows a day at a salary of twelve dollars per week. The following year he met Wilhelmina Beatrice Rahner, an eighteen-year-old girl from Brooklyn. It was love at first sight, and within two weeks they were married. The marriage marked the beginning of "the Houdinis," with Bess, as his wife was called, being an attractive addition to his magic act.

Five years of hardship and struggle followed. For very little money, Harry and Bess gave thousands of shows in front of the toughest and most demanding kinds of audiences. Houdini used these years of struggle to polish and perfect the escape act that only a few years later would make him a headliner at fabulous salaries in the most important theaters in the world.

Just how Houdini began to concentrate on escapes is not known. One theory is that, again, he was influenced by reading a rare book he had come upon in which the author revealed how a person could escape from rope ties, metal collars, and knotted and sealed bags. When, at the turn of the century, he finally began to get the recognition he had struggled so hard for, Houdini came to be known as "the handcuff king." The idea of escaping from handcuffs was not a new one, but Houdini's brilliant idea of allowing people to bring real cuffs to restrain him made him famous for his handcuff escapes.

Then, too, Houdini was a master at handling the press and gaining publicity for himself. There was scarcely a town where Houdini played that he was not on the front pages of the local newspaper. Here, for example, is an excerpt from an article which appeared in a Virginia newspaper in April 1900.

> Houdini, in an exhibition given in the City Hall yesterday before Chief Howard, Captain Angle, and many other of the police force, puzzled these officers and some thirty or forty other gentlemen who were present. Houdini seems to have fairly won his title, the King of Handcuffs. He stripped himself of all clothing so it could not be charged that he had keys or springs concealed about his person, and

with his mouth sealed with plaster, and bound with a handkerchief, he removed four pairs of irons that had been placed upon him by Captain Angle.

Dr. C.W.P. Brock attended to thoroughly closing the "King's" mouth, and then Captain Angle placed the shackles upon the performer. Irons were put not only upon Houdini's wrists, but also upon his feet, and then his hands were shackled to his legs. Houdini did not remove the irons in the presence of spectators, but got behind a chair over which a rug was thrown. However, he was almost entirely within the sight of those in the room, and many even saw the performer as he worked upon his shackles. In 2 minutes he stepped from behind the chair holding the four pairs of irons in his hands. It was simply a wonderful exhibition and every one in the room admitted that the King of Handcuffs was one too many for them...

Houdini used the "naked test" jailbreak as a top publicity stunt for many years to come. At times he added such newsworthy pranks as opening all the other cells in the jail and moving the prisoners to different cells or opening the cell in which his clothes were locked and appearing in front of his audience not only free but fully dressed.

One of Houdini's most widely reported challenge escapes was from a prison van during his tour of Russia in 1903. The portable steel cells, lined with zinc and mounted on a wagon body, were pulled by a team of horses used to transport prisoners. To this day, it is not known how Houdini managed to escape the van. One theory is that Bess had the necessary tools hidden in her mouth and passed them to the naked Houdini as she gave him a farewell kiss.

In addition to the standard jail escape, Houdini devised special escapes that were offered to him as challenges by merchants and local organizations in each city he played. He escaped from paper bags (without tearing the paper), zinc-lined piano boxes, padded cells, U.S. mail pouches, coffins, straitjackets of many different designs, a large football made by a local sporting goods manufacturer, a roll-top desk, various burglar-proof safes, wet packs used to subdue the violently insane, a plate glass box, a diving suit, and various types of steel boilers.

Tragically, the challenges that brought him worldwide fame and fortune also brought him death. In October 1926, Houdini was playing in Montreal. He was backstage in his dressing room preparing for the show when there was a knock at the door. Two college students had come to see the great Houdini and especially to find out for themselves if one of the well-publicized stories about the illusionist was true. It was said that Houdini had such control over all of his muscles that he could sustain punches to his stomach without injury. When asked about this by the boys, Houdini agreed that he was able to do this. Suddenly, before Houdini had time to brace himself, one of the students punched him hard in the stomach. Houdini recovered from the force of the blow, and the students left.

It is very odd that Houdini, who always made one hundred per cent sure of the success of each of his feats, would let two strange men into his dressing room and then let one of them punch him. But this is what happened on that fateful day of October 21, 1926. Houdini dismissed the incident. But, unknown to him, the unexpected blow had ruptured his appendix. Through sheer will power he continued to perform in ever-increasing pain, but after a performance a few days later he collapsed.

On Halloween of 1926, the most famous magician who had ever lived passed quietly away.

---

1 **Understanding the Reading.** Put the letter of the best answer on the line to the left.

__b__ 1. This reading is an excerpt from a(n) _____.

(a) autobiography (c) essay
(b) biography (d) short story

__c__ 2. Houdini's motive in running away from home when he was twelve was _____.

(a) to become a magician (c) to help his family
(b) to escape family pressures (d) to seek adventure

__b__ 3. Henning's reason for writing about Dr. Lynn is _____.

(a) to cite evidence of the good relationship Houdini enjoyed with his father
(b) to describe an early influence on Houdini's chosen career
(c) to reveal the tricks used by an illusionist
(d) to show how audiences responded to illusionists

__b__ 4. We can guess that Houdini's first meeting with the woman who was to become his wife was _____.

(a) business-like (c) stormy
(b) romantic (d) uneventful

__a__ 5. Which of the following did *not* contribute to Houdini's fame as "the Handcuff King"?

(a) He greatly admired Robert-Houdin, the fabulous French magician.
(b) He dared people to present him with seemingly impossible challenges.
(c) He knew how to use publicity in order to broadcast his talent.
(d) He worked hard to perfect his talent as an illusionist.

__b__ 6. In which sentence does Henning present information as if he is *not* certain that it is true?

(a) "...his friend suggested that if he added the letter "i" to Houdin's name, it would mean *like Houdin*..."
(b) "Houdini purchased this illusion (reportedly for $75)..."
(c) "To this day, it is not known how Houdini managed to escape the van."
(d) "It was said that Houdini had such control over all of his muscles that he could sustain punches...without injury."

__a__ 7. In the newspaper excerpt, which of the following is *not* a statement of opinion?

(a) "...he was almost entirely within the sight of those in the room..."
(b) "Houdini...puzzled these officers and some thirty or forty other gentlemen who were present."
(c) "Houdini seems to have fairly won his title, the King of Handcuffs."
(d) "It was simply a wonderful exhibition and every one in the room admitted..."

__d__ 8. Probably the greatest stumbling block to Henning in researching the facts about Houdini's life was _____.

(a) accounts reported in the newspapers
(b) finding the books that inspired Houdini
(c) his lack of knowledge about magic
(d) the false information provided by Houdini's family

d 9. Based on this reading, Henning's main intent is ____.

(a) to add his own knowledge to the Houdini legend
(b) to explore the mysterious circumstances regarding Houdini's death
(c) to expose the truth about the real Houdini
(d) to present information about Houdini's life

a 10. Henning's attitude toward Houdini seems to be one of ____.

(a) admiration (c) neutrality
(b) disbelief (d) scorn

2 **What Do You Think?** Answer the following questions in good sentence form.

1. If you had been a member of the audience during one of Houdini's performances, would you hope that he could escape his latest challenge or would you hope that someone had finally outsmarted him? Include at least one reason to help to explain your answer.

____

____

____

2. If Houdini were performing today, do you think he would enjoy the same degree of fame and fortune that he enjoyed in his own lifetime? Be sure to include reasons to support your opinion.

____

____

____

____

____

David copper

3

Synonyms. *Synonyms* are words that have similar meanings. From the choices listed, choose the best synonym for the word in bold-faced type and write it on the line to the right. The first one has been done to get you started.

1. **exhibition:**	commotion	discovery	display	drama	display
2. **shackle:**	ambush	confine	entangle	punish	______
3. **rupture:**	burst	decay	enlarge	separate	______
4. **publicize:**	advertise	expose	narrate	pronounce	______
5. **fascinated:**	appreciative	attentive	mindful	spellbound	______
6. **astonishing:**	amazing	attractive	pleasant	mysterious	______
7. **worldwide:**	earthy	foreign	national	universal	______
8. **legend:**	biography	memoirs	myth	rumor	______
9. **feat:**	achievement	exception	extrication	illusion	______
10. **extricate:**	discharge	disentangle	disjoin	dismember	______
11. **subdue:**	overload	overpower	overturn	overwork	______
12. **shrouded:**	deathly	disorderly	hidden	treacherous	______
13. **plunge:**	dive	glide	orbit	whirl	______
14. **sustain:**	dismiss	overwhelm	support	welcome	______

4 **Names That Have Made the Dictionary.** Houdini is not the only person whose name has become a household word. With the help of a dictionary, use the names listed below to complete the sentences. Then, on the lines to the left, write the word that is derived from each name. In some cases, the word is exactly the same as the person's name. The first one has been done to get you started.

Braille	Fahrenheit	Macintosh	Poinsett
Derick	Lynch	Nicot	Sandwich

braille ______ 1. Blinded in 1812, the Frenchman Louis Braille ______ later devised a system of printing for the blind which bears his name.

poinsett ______ 2. Joel R. ______, having served as a special minister to Mexico during the middle 1800s, returned to the United States with these large, flaming flowers, which have become a favorite decoration during the Christmas season.

Mocintosh ______ 3. In 1823, Charles ______ established a factory in Scotland to make waterproof fabrics from rubber, and the raincoats made of this material quickly became popular.

Fahrenleit ______ 4. Gabriel David ______, in the early years of the 18th century, constructed the first mercury thermometer, which made recording temperatures much easier.

Lynch ______ 5. Colonel Charles ______ of Virginia, a county court justice, may have given us this word. During the Revolutionary War he was unable to safely transport people accused of felonies to the court in Williamsburg, so he set up a court, tried the cases, and imposed punishment himself.

Shandwich ______ 6. The fourth Earl of ______, an Englishman of the 18th century, had such a passion for gambling that during one 24-hour session, he refused to stop for any meals and instead ordered his servant to bring him slices of bread with roast beef nested between them.

Derick ______ 7. This hoisting device was named after Godfrey ______, a famous 17th century hangman at an English prison, who invented a gallows that used this device.

Nicot ______ 8. Jean ______, the French ambassador to Portugal in 1560, was curious about some seeds that had been brought from America. He sent some of the seeds on to France where they were planted, producing the first tobacco raised in Europe. His name was given to the poisonous substance found in tobacco.

5 **Challenges.** Perhaps these challenges are not so dramatic as Houdini's, but you might enjoy trying them out on your friends anyway. First, you must put the steps of each challenge in a sensible order. The first challenge has been started for you.

1\. ______ Add that only *one* glass can be moved.

______ Then challenge your friend to rearrange the glasses so that each full glass is next to an empty glass.

______ When your friend gives up, pick up the middle glass, drink the water, and put the glass back in its place.

______ Pour water into the three middle glasses.

______ Set five glasses side by side on a table.

2\. ______ After your friend gives up, cut through one of the loops of the bow, and you've successfully met the challenge.

______ Challenge your friend to cut the string without letting the cup fall to the floor.

______ Mention that the cup is not to be touched either.

______ Now hand your friend a pair of scissors.

______ Hang a china cup from a doorknob by looping a piece of string through the handle of the cup and tying the string around the doorknob in a bow.

3\. ______ Be sure to use the word *figures* and not *numbers*.

______ However, when you write them for your puzzled friend, write:

$$\begin{array}{r} 17 \\ 1 \\ 1 \\ 1 \\ \hline 20 \end{array}$$

______ State that you can write five odd figures that will add up to twenty.

______ The figures you will use are 1, 1, 1, 1, and 7.

______ Your friend will be puzzled because, as everybody knows, an odd number of odd numbers always adds up to an odd number.

Lesson 2

Mirror, Mirror, on the Wall...

Words for Study

fascination	economies	initiation	mutilate
primitive	exotic	identification	petroleum
civilized	techniques	Melanesia	perception
anthropologist	symbolic	missionaries	self-portrait

Mirror, Mirror, on the Wall...

Throughout recorded history, men and women have had a fascination for changing their appearance by using cosmetics and other forms of body art. *Cosmetics*, as defined by the United States Federal Food, Drug and Cosmetic Act, is a word which can be equally applied to African, Asian, and Western body art: "articles intended to be rubbed, poured, sprinkled or sprayed on, introduced into, or otherwise applied to the human body or any part thereof for cleansing, beautifying, promoting attractiveness, or altering the appearance."

In this reading, the author describes the role cosmetics has played in different cultures. The author also presents some interesting thoughts for us to consider in his discussion of the concepts *primitive* and *civilized.*

* * *

I am attempting a description of the decoration of the human body in various cultures, whether by painting, tattooing, or otherwise changing its surface. As an anthropologist, one of my main aims is to lessen the traditional gap between the primitive and the civilized, and a comparison of body art is as good a means as any other.

I must apologize at once for using such terms as *primitive* and *civilized.* I use *primitive* to refer to people who live in small groups, who can neither read nor write, and who have very simple economies. The word *civilized* means "having a highly-developed society or culture." I also use *Western* to refer to those societies which in general pursue a European or American way of life. And I shall be describing Western practices of body decoration as measurements by which we can understand *exotic*—that is *different*—techniques. I believe that fashionable Western techniques of make-up, plastic surgery and hair-styling differ very little from those of primitive body art, except that primitive body decoration has more religious and social functions. In Western societies, paint and pattern do not celebrate the physical and social body, but rather are used to conform to fashion.

Non-Western body art is a symbolic statement in which the decoration sends messages about groups or individuals. The native Australians paint their bodies as part of their religion. For religious ceremonies, people use the patterns and colors that have been passed down from generation to generation. In everyday life, however, they make themselves attractive by painting themselves with any pattern and any color. A whole family may spend long hours improving each other's appearance, painting detailed designs on different parts of the body. Parents paint their children and display them proudly to other members of the group.

Before coming into much contact with Europeans, many North American Indians also delighted in transforming the natural body into a work of art. One northwestern group, the Haida, painted their faces daily for cosmetic purposes. For dances and special ceremonies, designs and colors were more carefully applied. Both the men and women of the Haida tribe wore earrings. If they were of high rank, royal crests were tattooed on their legs and arms.

The Thompson Indians, who lived between the Rocky Mountains and the Thompson River, were masters at cosmetic decoration. As a rule, individuals painted themselves. Water or sheets of mica were used as looking glasses. Most young people painted their faces for cosmetic reasons, experimenting with designs and colors, even changing their face and body patterns several times a day.

Each Thompson Indian acquired a guardian spirit during initiation ceremonies and took on the qualities connected with that guardian spirit. During the winter dances, the singers and dancers painted themselves with designs representing the individual's guardian spirit, the spirit having indicated to him the designs to paint. Warriors painted their bodies before going to war. Each warrior had an individual pattern, but in all the paintings, the main idea was to bring good luck to the warrior and ill luck to the enemy.

As the Indians of North and South America increased their contact with Europeans, most stopped painting themselves. The Indians looked on the pale-faced Europeans with scorn, but unable to explain the importance and value of their body art, they abandoned it. Today, body painting has all but disappeared as a living art among the North American Indians, and in South America it is still popular only among the more remote tribes.

Another cosmetic practice that has enjoyed widespread use is tattooing. Like painting, tattooing has been used for many different reasons: decoration, identification, magic, an ordeal to prove courage, initiation ceremonies, a way to prevent old age and illness, relationships with guardian spirits, and a property mark on slaves.

The great chiefs of New Zealand had their faces and their bodies covered with tattooed designs of delicate beauty, and all free men were permitted to do the same. Personal, individual designs were made on men's faces, which made them easily noticed in war and attractive to women. A face tattoo was also a kind of personal signature, and they believed that their personalities were reflected in these face patterns. When the chiefs signed deeds of land sales to Europeans, instead of a signature or a cross, they drew their face patterns, without the aid of mirrors and with great ease.

In many parts of the world, but particularly in Africa and in Melanesia, a group of islands in the South Pacific, young girls are tattooed in recognition of their important roles as future wives and mothers in the community. Tattooing was also used on other important occasions. In 19th century Hawaii, for instance, the tips of the tongues of women were tattooed as a sign of mourning the death of a chief or some other tragic event.

Tattooing died out in Europe in the Middle Ages because the Christian church disapproved of it. But it flourished again after contact with the Far East and the South Seas in the 19th century. England's Duke of York (later King George V), his brother the Duke of Clarence, and Tsar Nicholas of Russia were all tattooed by the same Japanese artist. For a time tattooing had an immense popularity in England. When Edward VII was crowned in 1901, many people, including Lady Randolph Churchill, had tattoos done with the royal arms or a patriotic motto.

Through the centuries, people in civilized cultures have tended to think that their cultures are superior to primitive cultures and that their practices are "natural" while those of others are "unnatural." Early travelers and missionaries who journeyed to the islands of the South Pacific and the remote regions of Africa expressed these views. Blind to their own powdered wigs and tight laces, these travelers and missionaries considered the decorated bodies of the people they met on their journeys as signs of savage and uncivilized behavior.

Our language helps to maintain this unnatural division between primitive and civilized societies. *We* have make-up, cosmetics, scents, creams, and dyes; *they* have twigs and swabs, animal fats and dyes. *We* have plastic surgery; *they* mutilate themselves. An anthropologist studying a South American Indian during a special ceremony describes the patterns of colored clay applied with pork fat and the ground charcoal dabbed around the eyes. It is highly unlikely that he would describe his wife's make-up in the same terms; yet she is most likely also wearing a red dye mixed with wax on her lips; blue, green or white pigments mixed with petroleum jelly on her eyelids, and soot and pig's fat on her brows and lashes.

To further explore the similarities between primitive and civilized societies, let us compare a New Guinea trader with an American business executive. The main goal of both these men is the same: to appear attractive so they can make the best deal. The old trader knows that he will not make a deal without artificial aids. He would not dream of setting out without his cosmetic kit. He attempts to make himself attractive to his business friends through the use of spells and cosmetics. He rubs himself with fragrant leaves and coconut oil, arranges his hair and draws designs on his face. Youthfulness and attractiveness are magically applied to his body in the form of scents, dyes, and paints.

Like the South Pacific trader, the American executive realizes that in our culture also, an ugly, old face cannot be a successful one. He must consider his clothes, his figure, and his wrinkles. The American businessman is beginning to use cosmetics for the same reasons as women do—to promote good health, or the appearance of good health, by artificial means. He turns to the hair surgeon, the cosmetic surgeon, and the make-up specialist with the idea of looking younger and rested. He uses beauty products to make him feel bold, rugged, and commanding. For both the New Guinea trader and the American businessman, cosmetics are magical aids to success in business.

It is the *belief* in the power of cosmetics that makes them effective, since both the New Guinea trader and American businessman believe that they are young and attractive. This feeling, in turn, injects self-confidence into their behavior.

Cosmetics help an individual's appearance, and as Tolstoy, a Russian writer, remarked, "Nothing has so marked an influence on the direction of a man's mind as his appearance, and not his appearance itself, so much as his conviction that it is attractive or unattractive." This is how we should understand the satisfaction of a man smeared with soot and ocher in the New Guinea mountains or of a woman smeared with soot and ocher in a Miami bar.

Attention to the body is an attempt to put on a new skin, a cultural as opposed to a natural skin. It is a basic need which is practiced among all the peoples of the world. The matter goes even deeper. Body painting, tattooing, even hair styles are concerned with the questions all human beings ask: "Who am I? Who are we?" As long as there is an attempt to find an answer, people will continue to make up. A sane perception of self is closely linked with a sane perception of the body. As we paint our eyes, trim our body hair, put on our ties, belts and ribbons, we are creating a self-portrait. Through decorating our bodies we are telling other people that we are special kinds of individuals.

'The Head of a Chief of New Zealand, the face curiously tataowd, or mark'd, according to their manner.' (From *Journal to the South Seas* by Sydney Parkinson, 1773.)

1 **Understanding the Reading.** Put the letter of the best answer on the line to the left.

_____ 1. The author of this article, Robert Brain, is an anthropologist. From your reading of this article, what do you think an anthropologist is?

(a) a tour guide
(b) a person who studies different cultures
(c) a fashion designer
(d) a make-up artist

_____ 2. When Brain states: "...one of my main aims is to lessen the traditional gap between the primitive and the civilized..." he means that one of his main aims is to _____ .

(a) teach primitive people to act the same way civilized people do
(b) point out the differences between primitive and civilized cultures
(c) show that primitive people have been around longer than civilized people
(d) show that primitive and civilized peoples are more alike than many of us believe

_____ 3. The fact that North American Indians, South American Indians, and native Australians painted their bodies suggests that body painting _____ .

(a) is limited to warm climates
(b) was more common in the Northern Hemisphere
(c) was once popular in many parts of the world
(d) was unknown to people living in Africa

_____ 4. Peoples lessened their use of body painting as they _____ .

(a) increased their contact with Western societies
(b) ran out of materials needed for body painting
(c) became more interested in tattooing
(d) stopped fighting with other tribes

_____ 5. Which of the following practiced tattooing?

(a) Hawaiian women
(b) New Zealand chiefs
(c) girls in Melanesia
(d) all of these people

_____ 6. Brain suggests that cosmetics used by both primitive and civilized people _____ .

(a) are made from similar materials
(b) can cause infection
(c) are difficult to remove
(d) often have unpleasant fragrances

_____ 7. One argument put forth by Brain is that _____ .

(a) primitive people are often more civilized than so-called advanced people
(b) both primitive and civilized people use cosmetics for the same reason, to make them look attractive
(c) primitive people are less vain than civilized people
(d) the use of cosmetics is a relatively new practice

_____ 8. Brain suggests that _____ .

(a) anthropologists who study primitive people are prejudiced
(b) the use of cosmetics is an example of mankind's foolishness
(c) as long as people are concerned with their sense of identity, they will use cosmetics
(d) the past culture of the North American Indians was more advanced than that of the present South Pacific groups

2 More about *We* and *They*.

1. Brain talks about *we* and *they* in terms of civilized and primitive cultures. Sometimes people in our own culture also talk about *we* and *they*. Briefly describe what *we* (the people in italicized type) might say about *they* in the following situations. The first one has been done to get you started.

Situation 1: Waiting to use the bathroom

A. A *teenage boy* waits outside the bathroom for his twin sister to finish getting ready for a date.

Girls waste so much time putting on make-up and looking at themselves in the mirror. We have better things to do with our time.

B. *His twin sister* waits outside the bathroom for him to finish getting ready in the morning.

Boys take forever getting ready to leave. We have better things to do in the morning.

Situation 2: Waiting for the phone

A. A *mother* waits for her son to finish talking on the phone.

B. *Her son* waits for his mother to finish talking on the phone.

Situation 3: Being disturbed by loud noises

A. *Nick Thompson* is awakened very early on a Saturday morning by his neighbor's loud hammering.

B. *His neighbor* is kept awake very late on Saturday night by the loud music coming from Nick's home.

2. Describe a *we* and *they* situation from your own experience.

____

____

____

____

3. What conclusions can you draw about *we* and *they* thinking?

____

____

____

____

3

Antonyms. *Antonyms* are words that are opposite in meaning. From the choices listed, choose the best antonym for the word in bold-faced type and write it on the line to the right.

1. **gradually:**	eventually	finally	justly	suddenly	________
2. **beautify:**	deprive	disfigure	overpower	shackle	________
3. **primitive:**	advanced	American	brand-new	natural	________
4. **portable:**	complex	fixed	heavy	inexpensive	________
5. **attentive:**	careless	hateful	indignant	uncivilized	________
6. **thrive:**	dwindle	endure	maintain	sustain	________
7. **rugged:**	frail	generous	humble	unskilled	________
8. **thrift:**	budget	economy	prosperity	wastefulness	________
9. **poised:**	disgraceful	heartless	jittery	unsuspecting	________
10. **stunning:**	abnormal	homemade	plain	uninformed	________
11. **seemingly:**	apparently	certainly	reportedly	usually	________
12. **relieve:**	confine	inflict	linger	sacrifice	________
13. **fascinated:**	annoyed	ignorant	indifferent	unconvinced	________
14. **gloss:**	dullness	heartiness	stubbornness	thickness	________

4 **The Suffix *-logy*.** The suffix *-logy* indicates the science, theory or study of; for example, *anthropology* is the study of the origin and of the physical, social, and cultural development of man. Use a dictionary to help you match the following *-logies* with the correct description.

archaeology
astrology
biology
ecology
etymology
geology
meteorology
pathology
psychology
sociology
theology
zoology

_______________ 1. the biological science of animals

_______________ 2. the science dealing with occurrences in the atmosphere, especially weather and weather conditions

_______________ 3. the science of life and life processes, including the study of structure, functioning, growth, origin, evolution, and distribution of living organisms

_______________ 4. the science of mental processes and behavior

_______________ 5. the science of relationships between organisms and their environment

_______________ 6. the scientific study of man's life and culture in the past

_______________ 7. the scientific study of the nature of disease, its causes, processes, development, and consequences

_______________ 8. the scientific study of the origin, history, and structure of the earth

_______________ 9. the study of human social behavior; especially, the study of institutions and the development of human society

_______________ 10. the study of the nature of God and religious truth

_______________ 11. the study of the origin and historical development of words

_______________ 12. the study of the positions and aspects of heavenly bodies with a view to predicting their influence on the course of human affairs

5 **More about Melanesia.** Use the map to answer the questions which follow.

The Three Main Pacific Island Groups The Pacific Islands can be divided into three main groups: (1) Melanesia, meaning *black islands;* (2) Micronesia, meaning *small islands*; and (3) Polynesia, meaning *many islands.* This grouping is based on the race and customs of the native peoples and on the islands' geography.

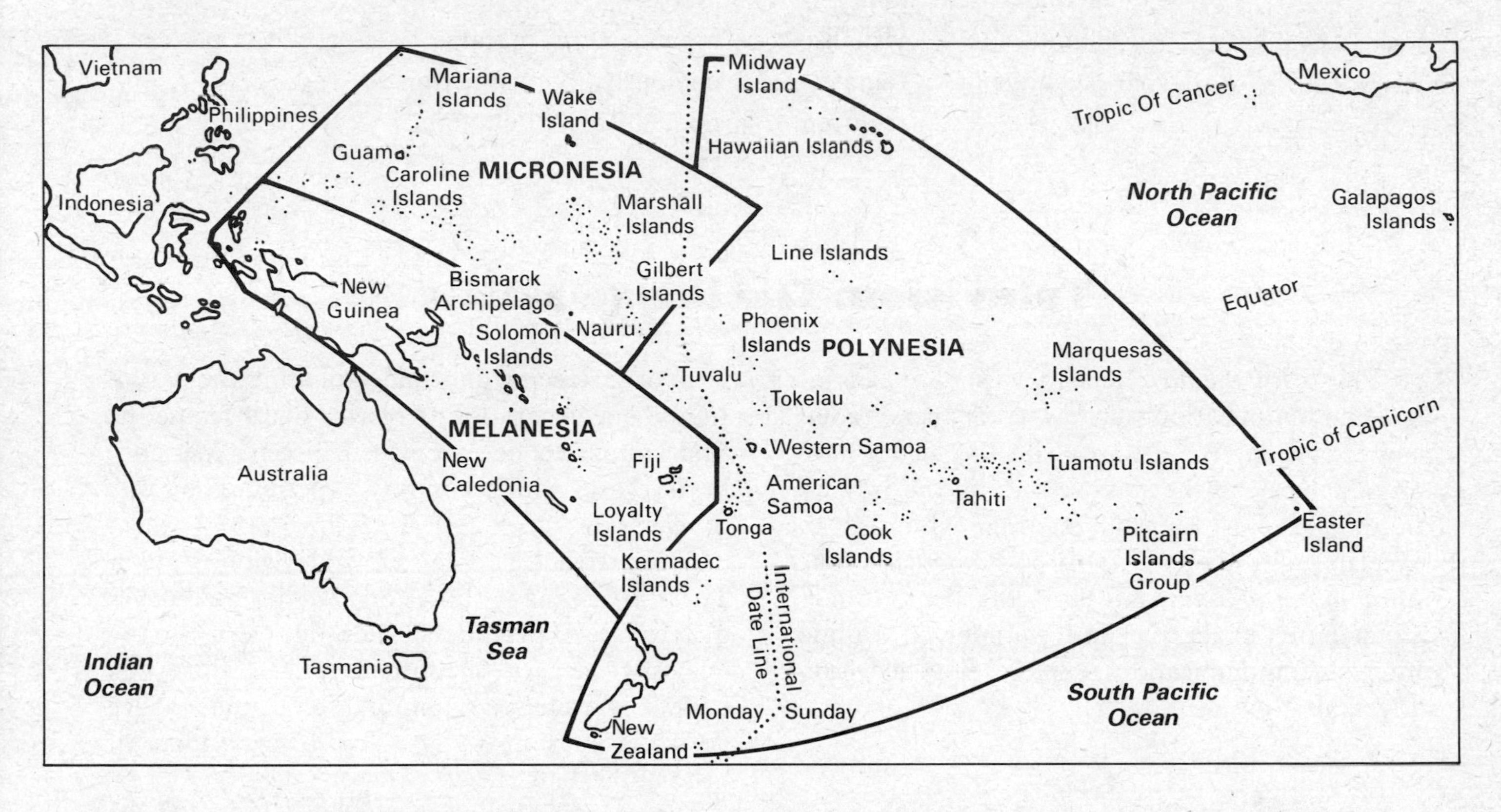

_____ 1. *Melanesia* means _____.

(a) black islands
(b) many islands
(c) Pacific islands
(d) small islands

_____ 2. Which of the following island groups is *not* part of Melanesia?

(a) Solomon Islands
(b) Loyalty Islands
(c) Fiji Islands
(d) American Samoa

_____ 3. To travel from New Caledonia to Indonesia, you would go _____.

(a) northeast (b) northwest (c) southeast (d) southwest

_____ 4. When it is Monday in Melanesia, it is only Sunday in _____.

(a) New Guinea
(b) the Bismark Archipelago
(c) the Cook Islands
(d) the Fiji Islands

_____ 5. Which of the following statements is false?

(a) Polynesia covers more territory than Melanesia.
(b) Melanesia is located in the Pacific Ocean.
(c) Western Samoa is west of Melanesia.
(d) New Zealand is not part of Melanesia.

Lesson 3

Television: The Image-Maker

Words for Study

media	edited	imagery	Sahara
elimination	visualize	immune	imitate
executive	fantasy	obviously	distinction
ballets	recurrent	nomads	fictional

Television: The Image-Maker

The term *media* refers to various means of mass communication, such as newspapers, radio, and television. What impact do the media have on our lives? on the way we see? on the way we think and feel? In this reading, which is an excerpt from his book, *Four Arguments for the Elimination of Television*, Jerry Mander, a former advertising executive and founder of Public Interest Communications, explores how television affects us.

* * *

In the early 1970s, a shocking burst of figures appeared in the newspapers.

It was reported that in the generation since 1945, 99 per cent of the homes in the United States had acquired at least one television set. On an average evening, more than eighty million Americans would be watching television. Thirty million of these people would be watching the same program. In special instances, one hundred million people would be watching the same program at the same time.

The average household had the set going more than six hours a day. If there was a child, the average was more than eight hours. The average person was watching for nearly four hours daily. And so, allowing eight hours for sleep and eight hours for work, roughly half of the adult nonsleeping, nonworking time was spent watching television.

As these numbers sank in, I realized that there had been a strange change in the way people received information. Even more, there had been a strange change in the way people were experiencing and understanding the world. In just one generation, America had become the first culture to have replaced direct experience in the world with secondary experiences by way of television.

I hear many people say, "Television is great. There are so many things on TV that we'd never otherwise experience." People were seeing television images of Borneo forests, European ballets, varieties of family life, distant police actions, current events, or re-creations of historical events.

Yet the television image of the Borneo forest or the news or historical events is surely not the experience of them. It is only the experience of sitting in a darkened room, staring at a flickering light, and taking in images which have been edited, cut, rearranged, sped up, slowed down, and confined in hundreds of ways.

More than any other single effect, television places images in our brains. Quite simply, an image is a mental picture. I have heard people say that they can't visualize; they can't make pictures in their heads. It's true that some people can do this more easily than others, but everyone does it.

If you believe yourself to be among those who can't, simply bring your mother or your best friend to mind. Have you done that? Can you see that person in your head? It's quite easy. If I ask you to recall your childhood bedroom, you can probably do that as well. The following list includes some of the ways in which human beings form images:

1. *Memory.* You can remember people's faces. You can visualize the place you work in.

2. *Imagination.* You can create images in your own mind.
3. *Daydreams or fantasy.* A kind of imagination that occurs while you are doing other things. These are pictures.
4. *Dreams.* You may not remember them, but practically everyone has them. These are pictures, too.
5. *After-image.* The movie is over, but the image remains in the head.
6. *Recurrent image.* The experience is over—for example, you have come home from work—but the face of the boss looms in your mind. You can't clear it out.

The image you carry in your mind can affect your actual physical body and your emotional state. To cite one example, an American doctor has done studies which show that when a person imagines himself running, small but measurable amounts of contraction actually take place in the muscles related to running.

Studies of cancer patients at a hospital in Oakland, California, provide us with another example of the power of imagery. The patient is instructed to picture his or her cancer and to imagine the immune system working the way it is supposed to—picking up the dead and dying cells. The doctors use photos of cells, photos of cancers, and X-ray photos of the person's own cancer to aid the process of visualizing. At some point, they ask the patients to visualize themselves totally well. The results of this technique have been amazingly successful.

How does our ability to form images relate to television? Today, television is the most important single source of images. When you are watching television, all categories of your own image-making give way to the television image. When you are watching TV, you are not daydreaming, or reading, or looking out the window at the world. You have opened your mind, and someone else's daydreams have entered. The images come from distant places you have never been, describe events you have never experienced, and are sent by people you don't know and have never met. Once their images are inside you, they imprint upon your memory. They become yours. What's more, the images remain permanently.

The question is this: Once television provides an image of a certain person, place, or time, what happens to your own image? Does it give way to the TV image or do you retain it? For example, let's take watching a football or baseball game. What comes to your mind—a game you have seen on television or one that you watched in person? If both images occur, which image seems stronger?

The answers vary on this point, but many people I have asked will report that the television image is the one which springs to mind first, if only because it was the most recent. Most will say the images rotate.

Now try to form images of these: Life under the sea. Life in an Eskimo village. A police shoot-out. Ben Franklin. An American farm family. The FBI. An emergency ambulance crew. The Old South.

Were you able to come up with images for any or all of these? It is extremely unlikely that you have experienced more than one or two of them personally. Obviously, the images were either out of your own imagination or else they were from the media. Can you identify which was which?

Most of the people in America right now would probably say that the images they carry in their minds of the Old South are from one of two television presentations: *Roots* and the movie *Gone with the Wind.* These were, as of this writing, the two most popular television shows in history, witnessed by more than 130 million people each. And none of the 130 million was actually in the Old South.

The same applies to descriptions of life-styles. What images do you use to understand the quality of life for farm laborers? Or artists? What images do you carry of Eskimo villagers or nomads in the Sahara Desert or Indians in the Amazon?

The point is that much of the information we think we have about the world in which we live comes not from images rooted in our own experience, but from television programs in which, again, the images are not natural but edited and arranged for us.

We are not only affected by these screen images; we also try to imitate them. Perhaps you have caught yourself kissing another person as you first saw kissing in the movies or television. My children have a phrase for this: "television kiss."

Most of us, however, did not make the distinction between television kissing and real kissing as we sat in darkened living rooms or theaters as children. Since we didn't see all that much *real* kissing, the media kiss became our image of kissing. We found ourselves producing that model of kiss later in life.

I was fourteen years old when I tried kissing for the first time. I imitated a movie star's kiss, but I didn't feel it. Only later did I realize that perhaps the movie star didn't feel it either; he was merely kissing the way the director said he should. So there I was imitating a kiss that was never real in the first place, worried that there might be something wrong with me for not having the appropriate feelings and failing to obtain the appropriate response.

Throughout the thousands of generations of human existence, whatever people saw with their eyes was concrete and reliable. Experience was directly between people and their natural environment. Nonprocessed. Not altered by other human beings.

In the modern world, information from the senses cannot be relied upon as before. We attempt to process artificial smells, tastes, sights, and sounds as if they can be real, but they are not real. Our senses are no longer reacting to information that comes directly from the source. They are reacting to processed information.

There is a widespread belief that some things on television are "real" and some things are not real. Furthermore, our society assumes that human beings are able to make the distinction between what is real and what is not real. But, according to the studies, this just isn't so. Both adults and children have a hard time separating what is television from what is real life.

The National Institute of Mental Health reports that a majority of adults use television to learn how to handle certain life problems. Even the knowledge that most television programs are fictional does not seem to prevent people from believing the images they present anyway, or at least gaining important impressions which lead to beliefs and values about how we should be.

In his novel *Being There*, the Polish writer Jerzy Kosinski describes a man who is born and raised in a house that he never leaves. He watches television constantly. In middle age, the hero is suddenly thrown out of the house into the city.

Attempting to deal with a world which he has seen only as reproduced on television, he tries to apply what he has learned from the set. He adopts television behavior. He tries to imitate the behavior of the people he has seen on the screen. However, because these people were only images to him, and he has never experienced *real* people, he does not know anything beyond the images.

He does not know about feelings, for example. He adopts the movements of the images, but he can't connect this with anything deeper inside himself. Because he has not exchanged feeling with a live human, his ability to feel has been stilled. He is a mechanical person, a robot. He is there physically, but like the television images, he is also not there.

Is there a chance this might really be happening to some twentieth century Americans?

---

1 **Understanding the Reading.** Mr. Mander uses a number of examples to support the points he is making. Briefly explain the point that Mr. Mander is making when he uses the following examples. The first one has been done to get you started.

1. Figures on television watching: The number of hours Americans watch TV each day indicates that TV is a major influence in our lives.

2. A TV show about the Borneo forest: ______________________________

3. Recurrent images: ______________________________

4. The Oakland study of cancer patients: ______________________________

5. The TV showing of *Gone with the Wind*: ______________________________

6. Mr. Mander's first experience with kissing: ______________________________

7. The report from the National Institute of Mental Health: ______________________________

8. The description of the novel *Being There*: ______________________________

2 **More on the Media.** Study the cartoon and answer the questions which follow.

1. Does Joseph Farris seem to agree or disagree with Mr. Mander's views in the reading? Be sure to include evidence from the reading to support your answer.

2. If a museum invited you to create a scene in which you portrayed the typical 20th century family, what would you choose for your display? Include as many details as you think are important so that your description will be easier to visualize.

3. What do you think the "person" at the 25th century display is looking at?

____

____

____

____

____

3 **Synonyms and Antonyms.** If the pair of words is similar in meaning, write *synonyms* on the line to the left. If the pair is opposite in meaning, write *antonyms*. The first one has been done to get you started.

antonyms 1. beautify——disfigure

__________ 2. executive——laborer

__________ 3. imitation——copy

__________ 4. fantasy——fiction

__________ 5. fascination——indifference

__________ 6. extricate——shackle

__________ 7. engrave——carve

__________ 8. neutral——prejudiced

__________ 9. nomad——wanderer

__________ 10. phase——aspect

__________ 11. publicize——conceal

__________ 12. reliable——trustworthy

__________ 13. retain——discard

__________ 14. similarity——distinction

__________ 15. visualize——imagine

__________ 16. worldwide——universal

4 The Suffix *-ist*.

The suffix *-ist* indicates a person who does, makes, produces, operates, plays, or is connected with a particular thing. Match each person at the left with the response he or she might make after having read the excerpt from Mr. Mander's book.

activist
alarmist
anthropologist
archaeologist
conformist
dramatist
etymologist
hypnotist
journalist
meteorologist
nonconformist
novelist

_______________ 1. "According to this author, you'd think television does the same thing I do every day—put people in trances."

_______________ 2. "Creating a cast of characters who live in modern America but have never seen a newspaper, radio, or television set would make a very interesting plot for my next book."

_______________ 3. "With all the free entertainment on television these days, not as many people go to see plays."

_______________ 4. "Maybe I can get an interview with the author and submit a story to my magazine publisher."

_______________ 5. "I'm so disturbed by this book that I'm going to organize a campaign and get everyone to write our Congresswoman immediately."

_______________ 6. "I want to read some more studies of cultures that don't have televisions before I draw any conclusions."

_______________ 7. "I wonder who first used the word *after-image* as it's used in this article?"

_______________ 8. "If I were living hundreds of years from now, I wonder what my reaction would be upon digging up a battered TV set among the ruins of some civilization."

_______________ 9. "If this guy is right, we'll all be robots in no time, and the whole world will come to an end!"

_______________ 10. "Maybe the author's right. But if all my friends watched TV and I didn't, I'd really feel left out."

_______________ 11. "Everyone watching TV is good enough reason for my not owning one."

_______________ 12. "Well, at least TV gives you a good idea of what the weather's going to be like tomorrow—if the forecast is correct."

5 A Familiar Television Phrase.

- The letters of the word in each box can be rearranged to form another word. Use the clues to help you figure out what that other word is.
- Then put the number of the clue into the circle. The circled numbers in each row and column will add up to 65.
- After you have figured out a word, write its first letter in the correct blank at the bottom of the page. When all the blanks are filled in, you will have spelled the familiar television phrase.
- To help you, the first and last words have been filled in.

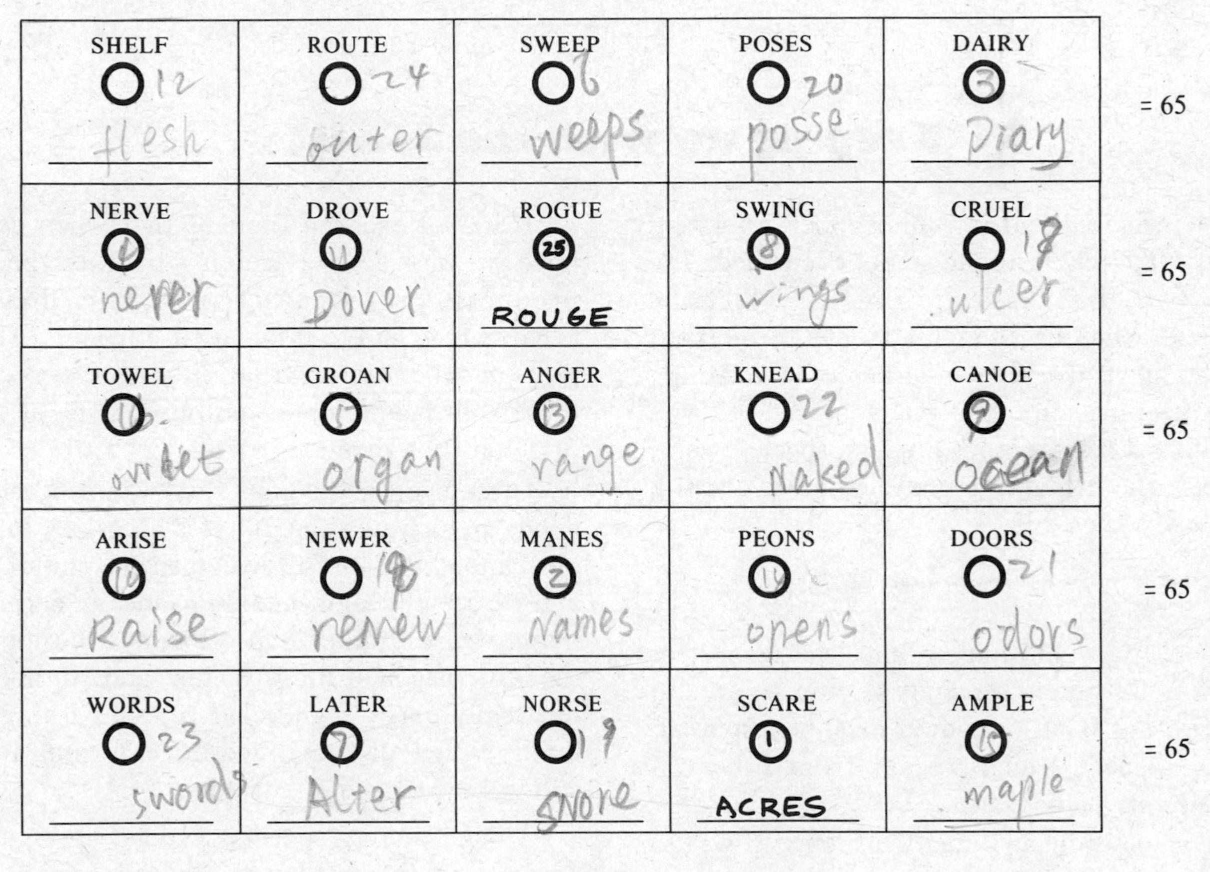

SHELF ○ ____	ROUTE ○ ____	SWEEP ○ ____	POSES ○ ____	DAIRY ○ ____	= 65
NERVE ○ ____	DROVE ○ ____	ROGUE ㉕ ROUGE	SWING ○ ____	CRUEL ○ ____	= 65
TOWEL ○ ____	GROAN ○ ____	ANGER ○ ____	KNEAD ○ ____	CANOE ○ ____	= 65
ARISE ○ ____	NEWER ○ ____	MANES ○ ____	PEONS ○ ____	DOORS ○ ____	= 65
WORDS ○ ____	LATER ○ ____	NORSE ○ ____	SCARE ① ACRES	AMPLE ○ ____	= 65
= 65	= 65	= 65	= 65	= 65	

1. Land units
2. Titles
3. A personal journal
4. "It's now or ______ ."
5. This accompanies the church choir.
6. Cries; sobs
7. To change
8. These help birds and planes fly.
9. The Atlantic or Pacific
10. An antonym for *lower*
11. The capital of Delaware
12. Skin
13. Where herds of cattle roam
14. Uncovers; unseals
15. A type of syrup
16. A baby owl
17. A painful stomach problem
18. An antonym for *cancel*
19. A sound made during sleep
20. The sheriff's men
21. Smells
22. Bare; nude
23. A fencer's weapon
24. An antonym for *inner*
25. A popular cosmetic

The familiar television phrase:

A _ _   _ _ _   _   _ _ _ _   _ _ _ _   _ _ _   _ _ _ _ _ _ R

1 2 3   4 5 6   7   8 9 10 11   12 13 14 15   16 17 18   19 20 21 22 23 24 25

Lesson 4

Keeping up with the Joneses

Words for Study

leisure	dishonorable	status	offensive
captives	manual	proportion	ingrained
ambition	instinct	contraption	frill
significant	necessities	inconvenient	accumulate

Keeping up with the Joneses

The American social philosopher Thorstein Veblen (1857-1929) wrote a book entitled *The Theory of the Leisure Class* in which he described what he thought people throughout the ages have worked at harder than anything else—"keeping up with the Joneses." As you read this excerpt from his highly respected work, consider whether or not what he had to say still holds true today.

* * *

In order to gain and to hold the respect of men, it is not enough merely to possess wealth or power. The wealth or power must be displayed, for the respect which we get from others is awarded only on evidence.

Throughout history, man's evidence of wealth has been based on owning things. There is every reason to believe that one of the earliest forms of ownership in history was the ownership of women by the able-bodied men of primitive communities. The original reason for the capture of women seems to have been their usefulness as trophies. This practice, in turn, gave birth to a form of ownership-marriage, resulting in households ruled by males.

This was followed by an extension of slavery to other captives, besides women, and by an extension of ownership-marriage to other women than those seized from the enemy. From the ownership of people, the concept of ownership extended itself to include the products of their industry. Thus, there arose the ownership of things as well as of persons.

It has often been thought that when people have struggled over goods—be they people, products, or property—they have done so because they had to in order to stay alive. This is not so. The motive that lies at the root of ownership is ambition—ambition to be as good or better than the next person.

Of course, in a community where nearly all goods are private property, it is necessary to earn a livelihood. Most of us live in such communities, and we are aware of the importance of earning a living. On the other hand, we must admit that the *basic* needs of food, shelter, and clothing do not really play a significant role in earning this living. When all is said and done, owning things still has the nature of a trophy.

These trophies—our possessions—provide the foundation on which we seek and gain respect from others. In order to stand well in the eyes of the community, it is necessary to come up to a certain commonly accepted standard of wealth. This standard is never very clearly defined; nevertheless it exerts its influence on us. Those members of the community who fall short of this undefined standard are considered failures.

To a great extent, the ambition to be as good as or better than everybody else determines what we decide to own. Just consider how often our purchases are based on "what everybody else has" or "what nobody else has yet." Besides this, the very means of livelihood we choose is also, to a great extent, based on this ambition to gain respect from others through ownership. Thus, "How much does it pay?" is often a far more important question when considering a new job than "What is the nature of the work?"

For those who do not have to labor in order to show their superior wealth, the concept of working for a living is a dishonorable one. From the days of the Greek philosophers right down to the present, a degree of leisure and freedom from hard work has been recognized as absolutely necessary in order to live a worthy or beautiful life. In some cultures, the sense of shamefulness of manual labor is so strong that it even overrides the instinct to survive. For instance, there are stories of certain Polynesian chiefs who preferred to starve to death rather than carry their food to their mouths with their own hands. There is also the story of a certain king of France whose servant happened to be absent one day. One of the duties of this servant was to move the king's throne when the heat from the roaring fireplace became too hot. Because the king refused to move his own throne, he suffered his royal person to be toasted beyond recovery.

For those who must labor in order to show wealth, the ways in which they gain and maintain respect take other forms. The desire here—and this applies to most of us since most of us have to work for a living—is not so much to be better, but to keep up with the accepted standards of what is considered decent ownership. Decency, in terms of our ambition to be respected, can be defined as owning goods which make us feel as if we enjoy a "higher" standard of living.

Quite often, these goods, which are usually wasteful, become more necessary to our sense of well-being than the basic necessities of life. For example, a family might delay repairing a faulty furnace in order to buy unnecessary furniture. This suggests that our concept of a high standard of living is based not on what we have, but on an ideal of ownership that is just beyond our reach. And, generally speaking, our ideals are set by the group of people who display just a bit more wealth than we do. Thus, the ambition to own more becomes a never-ending activity.

Perhaps no method of putting ownership on display provides such a fine example of showy and wasteful spending as dress. The clothes that we wear have always given an indication of our social status to all observers at first glance. And probably at no other point is our sense of shabbiness so keenly felt if we fall short of the standard set by society as in the matter of dress.

We not only buy clothes to impress others; we strive to buy as expensive clothes as we can. Inexpensive clothes are regarded as "cheap and nasty" without our even being conscious of the fact that we have passed this judgment. We tend to find things beautiful somewhat in proportion to their cost.

The function of dress as evidence of an ability to pay does not end with simply showing that the wearer consumes goods that have nothing whatsoever to do with physical comfort. Dress can also show that the wearer is not under the necessity of earning a livelihood or that, if a livelihood is involved, the wearer does not have to do manual labor.

The dress of women goes much farther than that of men in demonstrating status. In China, for example, it was once the custom to bind the feet of girls from the wealthier families. Because the feet could not grow properly, the girls grew to become women who could barely walk, thus indicating that they did not have to work. The Western version of this custom is the high heel which makes any manual work extremely difficult, and thus shows observers that the wearer is free from this type of labor. In the last century, the corset was commonly worn by fashionable women in spite of the fact that it did nothing to improve their appearance. A corset, for the benefit of modern readers who might have never heard of such a contraption, is an extremely tight-fitting undergarment. What this painful undergarment did offer, however, was an announcement to the world that its wearer did not have to work; for corsets were so uncomfortable that they made women unfit for work.

Dress must not only be obviously expensive and inconvenient to wear; it must at the same time be up-to-date. It is not known exactly how the custom of changing fashions originally started. What is obvious, however, is that if clothing is permitted to be popular for only a brief time, the wasteful buying of clothes will be greatly increased.

The same wastefulness that is apparent in fashionable clothing can be easily observed in other areas of buying as well. What is to be remembered is that this wastefulness has a strong effect on our beliefs about what is honest, beautiful, or useful.

In the matter of beauty and usefulness, beauty is usually the key factor, *but* beauty is often defined as expensiveness. Sometimes, beauty and expensiveness go hand in hand, as is the case with gold. Yet the usefulness of gold is due less to its beauty than to the fact that it is expensive. To use a not-so-beautiful example, the shine on a successful businessman's expensive shoes is no more beautiful than the shine on a beggar's threadbare sleeve. Yet the first is considered beautiful while the latter is considered highly offensive.

It is a well-known fact that shoppers are guided more by the finish and workmanship of the goods than by any signs of lasting usefulness. Goods, in order to sell, must have the marks of decent expensiveness in addition to usefulness. This, of course, makes each item more costly and leads us to believe that cheaper goods are automatically poorer in quality.

So completely has the habit of approving the expensive and disapproving the inexpensive been ingrained into our thinking that we automatically insist upon at least some measure of wasteful expensiveness in the goods we buy. Thus, it has come about that there are today no goods supplied anywhere which do not contain some unnecessary frill or feature in greater or lesser degree. Any consumer who wishes to insist on the elimination of all wealth symbols from his purchases would be unable to supply his most insignificant wants in the modern marketplace.

Adapted from *The Theory of the Leisure Class* by Thorstein Veblen. Used by permission of New American Library.

1 **Understanding the Reading.** Put the letter of the best answer on the line to the left.

_____ 1. According to Thorstein Veblen, our possessions have value for us when _____.
(a) they are displayed
(b) they are useful
(c) we have had to work hard for them
(d) we have not had to work hard for them

_____ 2. Veblen presents his discussion of women as trophies in primitive communities as _____.
(a) biased opinion
(b) false assumption
(c) proven fact
(d) reasonable theory

_____ 3. According to Veblen, _____ is at the heart of our desire for possessions.
(a) advertising (b) ambition (c) comfort (d) survival

_____ 4. Veblen defines ambition as the desire _____.
(a) to avoid manual labor
(b) to succeed in one's chosen career
(c) to enjoy at least an acceptable social status
(d) to use one's abilities to the fullest

_____ 5. According to Veblen, the standard of wealth a person must reach to gain the respect of others is _____.
(a) comical (b) fair (c) unimportant (d) vague

_____ 6. Which example is *not* used by Veblen to demonstrate how people have scorned labor throughout the ages?
(a) a French king (b) Chinese women (c) businessmen (d) the Greeks

_____ 7. According to Veblen, our sense of what is beautiful is determined by _____.
(a) commercials (b) cost (c) education (d) income

_____ 8. Veblen maintains that most of our purchases contain at least one _____ feature.
(a) shabby (b) tasteful (c) thoughtless (d) unnecessary

_____ 9. If Veblen's ideas are correct, the consumer who wishes to avoid all status symbols in his purchases would probably _____.
(a) have a hard time finding anything to buy
(b) have no impact on the buying habits of others
(c) buy well-made clothes
(d) have more time for important pursuits

_____ 10. The tone of this excerpt from *The Theory of the Leisure Class* is _____.
(a) amusing (b) critical (c) neutral (d) questioning

2 **What Do You Think?** Answer the following questions in good sentence form. Be sure to include reasons or examples in your answers.

1. If Thorstein Veblen were alive today, what do you think his reaction would be upon entering a modern department store or supermarket?

____

____

____

____

2. Do you think Veblen is correct—that our main ambition is displaying our possessions in order to prove that we're as good as or better than everyone else? Explain.

____

____

____

____

____

3. Imagine inviting Mr. Veblen into your home and giving him permission to throw out three of your possessions which he considered examples of wasteful spending. List three items he might throw out. After each item, write an objection you might offer in which you explain why the item is really necessary to your well-being.

Item	Objection
1. ____________	______________________________
	______________________________
2. ____________	______________________________
	______________________________
3. ____________	______________________________
	______________________________

3

Word Relationships. On the line to the left, write the letter of the answer that best completes each statement.

_____ 1. Houdini is to illusionist as _____.

(a) Capricorn is to equator
(b) Edison is to genius
(c) Macintosh is to anthropologist
(d) Veblen is to immigrant

_____ 2. Meteorology is to weather as _____.

(a) etymology is to dictionary
(b) pathology is to corpse
(c) psychology is to behavior
(d) zoology is to microscope

_____ 3. Hawaii is to Polynesia as _____.

(a) Fiji is to Micronesia
(b) Guam is to Melanesia
(c) Tahiti is to Polynesia
(d) Tasmania is to Indonesia

_____ 4. Petroleum is to fuel as _____.

(a) chloroform is to hospital
(b) commercial is to media
(c) derrick is to construction
(d) straitjacket is to contraption

_____ 5. Koran is to Moslem as _____.

(a) Bible is to Christian
(b) marriage is to ritual
(c) birth is to baptize
(d) synagogue is to Jew

_____ 6. Ambassador is to government as _____.

(a) captive is to imprisonment
(b) ecologist is to environment
(c) missionary is to church
(d) Haida is to Indian tribe

_____ 7. Midway is to island as _____.

(a) Mecca is to city
(b) Norse is to country
(c) Polynesia is to continent
(d) Vietnam is to colony

_____ 8. Aspect is to phase as _____.

(a) ambition is to will power
(b) recurrent is to sustained
(c) scoundrel is to rogue
(d) status is to superiority

_____ 9. Accumulate is to distribute as _____.

(a) attach is to engage
(b) civilize is to tame
(c) disentangle is to snare
(d) mutilate is to eliminate

_____ 10. Budapest is to Hungary as _____.

(a) Honolulu is to Hawaii
(b) Teheran is to Iran
(c) Montreal is to Canada
(d) Oslo is to Sweden

4 **The Suffix *-ism*.** The suffix *-ism* indicates a practice, characteristic behavior, system, theory, or condition of being. Match the *isms* listed below with the situations they best describe. Refer to a dictionary for any words you are not sure of. The first one has been done to get you started.

capitalism	heroism	materialism
cynicism	hypnotism	patriotism
✓escapism	idealism	skepticism
favoritism	individualism	terrorism

escapism 1. In order to avoid doing chores he disliked, Godfrey often convinced himself that he was exhausted and lay down to take a nap.

__________ 2. Believing that people are basically selfish, Gail distrusted anyone who enjoyed doing favors for others without expecting a reward in return.

__________ 3. Charles never went along with the crowd; instead he did exactly what he wanted to do—when he wanted to do it.

__________ 4. When Chris saw the man fall into the path of the oncoming subway train, he jumped onto the tracks and rescued him.

__________ 5. Wanting desperately to return to his homeland, the man hijacked a plane and held the passengers hostage for two days.

__________ 6. Jack spent every penny he had trying to "keep up with the Joneses" and never had a cent left to give to charity.

__________ 7. Because Aunt Martha liked Sally better than her other nieces, she gave her expensive birthday presents and sent the others only cards.

__________ 8. Ehrich never regretted immigrating to the United States where, through hard work over the years, he had built his company from a one-person operation to one that employed 500 people.

__________ 9. Tired of his addiction to nicotine, Scott asked his psychiatrist to put him into a trance and make him kick the cigarette habit.

__________ 10. When Joyce announced that she was going to turn over a new leaf and stop spending every cent she earned, her sister said, "Oh, really? Well, we'll just have to see."

__________ 11. Harry truly believed that people never committed acts of evil on purpose and envisioned a world in which love would conquer all.

__________ 12. Every Fourth of July, Jack Jefferson hung the American flag from his porch before leaving to march in the parade.

5 **Spelling Check.** In each of the sentences below, one underlined word may be misspelled. Write that word, spelled correctly, on the line. If all the words in the sentence are correct, write *correct* on the line.

________________ 1. The respected etymologist, Charles Earle Funk, received a letter one day in which the origen of the expression "keeping up with the Joneses" was explained.

________________ 2. The letter was from Arthur R. "Pop" Momand, and the folowing sentences are an abridged version of his letter.

________________ 3. Here is how it happened: At the age of 23 I was making $125 a week (good money in those days, with no income tax). I married and moved to Long Island, joined a country club, rode horseback daily, and had a maid.

________________ 4. Well, it was not long until the butcher, the baker, ect., were knocking gently but firmly on the old front door. In the end we pulled up stakes, headed for New York and moved into a cheap apartment.

________________ 5. Our Long Island experience was a rude awakening, but I saw the humorus side of it. We had been living far beyond our means. I also noted that most of our friends were doing the same.

________________ 6. I decided it would make good comic-strip material, so I drew six strips. At first I thought of calling it "Keeping up with the Smiths," but finally decided on "Keeping up with the Joneses."

________________ 7. "Keeping up with the Joneses" was launched—and little did I realize it was to run for twenty-eight years and take us across the Atlantic fourty-two times.

________________ 8. The feature was released in February of 1913 and appeared first in the *New York Globe*, *Chicago Daily News*, *Boston Globe*, *Philadelphia Bullitin* and ten minor papers.

________________ 9. The strip gained in popularity each year; it appeared in two-reel comedies, was put on as a musical comedy, and published in a carton book.

________________ 10. After twenty-eight years on the old treadmill, I tired of it. Today I paint portrats, landscapes—and, yes, I hate to admit it, we are still trying to "keep up with the Joneses."

Lesson 5

While the Auto Waits

Words for Study

hovered	humility	luxuries	impels
trivial	humanity	gesture	Pierre
distinguished	modestly	monotony	parallel
recipient	marionettes	accurate	Arabian

While the Auto Waits

by O. Henry

Promptly at the beginning of twilight, there came again to that quiet corner of that quiet small park the girl in gray. She sat upon a bench and read a book, for there was yet half an hour left in which one could still read outside.

To repeat: Her dress was gray and quite plain. A large-meshed veil masked her hat and also her face which shone through it with a calm and unconscious beauty. She had come there at the same hour on the previous day and on the day before that, and there was someone in the park who knew it.

The young man who knew it hovered near, offering small prayers to that great lady, Luck. His prayers were rewarded; for, in turning a page, her book slipped from her fingers and bounded from the bench a full yard away.

The young man pounced upon it with eagerness and returned it to its owner with the kind of style that seems to flourish in parks and public places—a mixture of manly politeness and hope and watchful respect for a policeman who might happen by. In a pleasant voice, he risked a trivial remark about the weather—a topic which is responsible for so much of the world's unhappiness—and stood poised for a moment, awaiting his fate.

The girl looked him over leisurely; at his ordinary, neat clothes and his features, which were not particularly distinguished.

"You may sit down, if you like," she said in a deep, rich voice. "Really, I would like you to sit down. The light is too bad for reading, and I would prefer to talk."

The recipient of Lady Luck's attention slid upon the seat by her side with ready obedience.

"Do you know," he said, speaking the formula with which park gentlemen begin their conversations, "that you are the most stunning girl I have seen in a long time? I had my eye on you yesterday. Didn't know somebody was bowled over by your beauty, did you, sweet thing?"

"Whoever you are," said the girl in icy tones, "you must remember that I am a lady. I will excuse the remark you have just made because the mistake was, doubtless, not an unnatural one—in your circle. I asked you to sit down; if the invitation leads to your rudeness, consider it withdrawn."

"I earnestly beg your pardon," pleaded the young man. His expression of satisfaction had changed to one of regret and humility. "It was my fault, you know—I mean there are girls in parks, you know—that is, of course, you don't know, but—"

"Drop the subject, please. Of course I know. Now, tell me about these people passing and crowding along these paths. Where are they going? Why do they hurry so? Do you think they're happy?"

The young man had promptly discarded his flirting role. His cue was now for a waiting part; he could not guess the new role he would be expected to play.

"It *is* interesting to watch them," he replied, studying her mood. "It is the wonderful drama of life. Some are going to supper and some to—er—other places, I guess. One wonders what their histories are."

"I don't," said the girl. "I'm not so curious. I come here to sit because here only can I be near the great, common, throbbing heart of humanity. Can you guess why I spoke to you, Mr.—?"

"Parkenstacker," said the young man. He now looked eager and hopeful.

"No," said the girl, holding up a slender finger and smiling slightly. "You would recognize it immediately. It is simply impossible to keep one's name out of print. Or even one's portrait. This veil and this hat of my maid furnish me with a disguise. You should have seen the chauffeur stare at it when he thought I wasn't looking. I spoke to you, Mr. Stackenpot—"

"Parkenstacker," corrected the young man modestly.

"—Mr. Parkenstacker, because I wanted to talk, for once, with a natural man—a man unspoiled by that hateful gloss of wealth and imagined superiority. Oh! you do not know how weary I am of it—money, money, money! And of the men who surround me, dancing like little marionettes all cut by the same pattern. I am sick of pleasure, of jewels, of travel, of society, of luxuries of all kinds."

"I always had an idea," the man said hesitatingly, "that money must be a pretty good thing."

"Perhaps. But when you have so many millions that—!" She concluded the sentence with a gesture of despair. "It is the monotony of it," she continued, "that bores me. Drives, dinners, theaters, dances. Sometimes the very tinkle of the ice in my champagne glass nearly drives me mad."

Mr. Parkenstacker looked innocently interested. "I have always liked," he said, "to read and hear about the ways of wealthy folks. I suppose I'm a bit of a snob. But I like to have my information accurate. Now, I had formed the opinion that champagne is cooled in the bottle and not by placing ice in the glass."

The girl gave a musical laugh of genuine amusement.

"You should know," she laughed, as if she were speaking to a slow-witted child, "that we of the non-useful class depend for our amusement upon breaking with custom. Just now, it is a fad to put ice in champagne."

"I see," admitted the young man humbly. "These special amusements of the inner circle do not become known to the common public."

"Sometimes," continued the girl, "I have thought that if I ever should love a man, it would be one of lowly station. One who is a worker and not a drone. But, doubtless, the claims of class and wealth will prove stronger than my desire. Just now I am chased by two. One is a Grand Duke from Germany. I think he has, or has had, a wife somewhere who has been driven mad by his cruelty. The other is an English Lord, so cold and heartless that I even prefer the cruelty of the Duke. What is it that impels me to tell you these things, Mr. Packenstaker?"

"Parkenstacker," breathed the young man. "Indeed, you cannot know how much I appreciate your telling me these things."

The girl looked at him with a calm, cool regard that suited the difference in their stations in life.

"What is your line of business, Mr. Parkenstacker?" she asked.

"A very humble one. But I hope to rise in the world. Were you really in earnest when you said that you could love a man of lowly position?"

"Indeed I was. No calling could be too humble were the man what I would wish him to be."

"I work," declared Mr. Parkenstacker, "in a restaurant."

The girl shrank slightly.

"Not as a waiter?" she said, a little pleadingly. "Labor is noble, but—"

"I am not a waiter. I am cashier in"—on the street they faced that bounded the opposite side of the park was the brilliant electric sign RESTAURANT—"I am cashier in the restaurant you see there."

The girl consulted a tiny watch set in a bracelet of rich design upon her left wrist and rose hurriedly. She thrust her book into a glittering bag for which, however, the book was too large.

"Why are you not at work?" she asked.

"I am on the night shift," said the young man. "It is yet an hour before I start. May I not hope to see you again?"

"I do not know. Perhaps—but the whim may not seize me again. I must go quickly now. There is a dinner and a box seat at the theater—and, oh! the same old round. Perhaps you noticed an automobile at the upper corner of the park as you came. One with a white body."

"And red running gear?" asked the young man, knitting his brows thoughtfully.

"Yes. I always come in that. Pierre waits for me there. He supposes me to be shopping in the department stores across the square. Imagine the chains binding the life in which we must deceive even our chauffeurs. Good night."

"But it is dark now," said Mr. Parkenstacker, "and the park is full of dangerous men. May I not walk—?"

"If you have the slightest regard for my wishes," said the girl firmly, "you will remain at this bench for ten minutes after I have left. Again, good night."

Swift and stately she moved away through the dusk. The young man watched her graceful form as she reached the pavement at the park's edge and turned up along it toward the corner where the automobile stood. Then he began to dodge and skim among the park trees and shrubbery in a course parallel to her route, keeping her well in sight.

When she reached the corner, she turned her head to glance at the automobile, and then passed it, continuing on across the street. Sheltered behind a cab, the young man followed her movements closely with his eyes. Passing down the sidewalk of the street opposite the park, she entered the restaurant with the blazing sign. The place was one of those glaring establishments where one may dine cheaply. The girl went to the back of the restaurant but soon reappeared without her hat and veil.

The cashier's desk was at the front. A red-haired girl on the stool climbed down, glancing angrily at the clock as she did so. The girl in gray mounted in her place.

The young man thrust his hands into his pockets and walked slowly back along the sidewalk. At the corner his foot struck a small, paperback volume lying there, sending it sliding to the edge of the grass. By its quaint cover, he recognized it as the book the girl had been reading. He picked it up carelessly and saw that its title was "New Arabian Nights." He dropped it again upon the grass, and stood there, undecided, for a minute. Then he stepped into the automobile, stretched out among the cushions, and said four words to his chauffeur:

"To the club, Henri."

1 **Understanding the Story.** Write the letter of the best answer on the line to the left.

______ 1. The girl most likely wore a veil ______ .

(a) for religious reasons
(b) to disguise herself
(c) to protect her complexion
(d) to shade her eyes

______ 2. Mr. Parkenstacker's prayer was probably a plea that ______ .

(a) he'd be granted an opportunity to meet the girl
(b) a police officer wouldn't interrupt his romantic pursuit
(c) the chauffeur wouldn't come to get him
(d) it wouldn't start to rain

______ 3. The girl excuses Mr. Parkenstacker's bold compliment because she believes ______ .

(a) all men are coarse and common
(b) all men begin conversations with young ladies in this way
(c) he is ignorant due to his social position
(d) he is mistaken about her social position

______ 4. Mr. Parkenstacker ceases to flirt with the girl because ______ .

(a) he decides to play "hard to get"
(b) his attention is drawn to the people passing by
(c) his interest in her is fading
(d) his strategy isn't working

______ 5. According to the girl, the most tiresome feature of wealth is ______ .

(a) marriage (b) romance (c) servants (d) the life style

______ 6. Mr. Parkenstacker's probable motive for declaring that he works in a restaurant is ______ .

(a) to make fun of the girl's employment
(b) to stall for more time
(c) to win the affection of the girl
(d) to offer sympathy for the girl's working conditions

______ 7. When Mr. Parkenstacker tells the girl that he is a cashier, she ______ .

(a) calls him a liar
(b) realizes that it's time to go to work
(c) feels ashamed that she has deceived him
(d) decides not to see him again

______ 8. Which of the following excerpts from "While the Auto Waits" has the *least* bearing on the plot?

(a) "...the weather—a topic which is responsible for so much of the world's unhappiness..."
(b) "It is the wonderful drama of life."
(c) "Just now, it is a fad to put ice in champagne."
(d) "To the club, Henri."

_______ 9. A synonym for *quaint* as in "By its quaint cover, he recognized it as the book the girl had been reading" is _____.

(a) costly (b) inexpensive (c) old-fashioned (d) ragged

_______ 10. We can guess that *New Arabian Nights* is a collection of _____.

(a) essays about wealth
(b) murder mysteries
(c) romantic adventures
(d) science fiction stories

2 **What Do You Think?** A *pretense* is a false appearance or action which is intended to deceive someone else. In "While the Auto Waits," for example, the girl's pretense is that of a wealthy lady of high society. Answer these questions about pretenses in good sentence form.

1. What is Mr. Parkenstacker's pretense and why do you think he chooses to act in this way?

____

____

____

____

2. What might have happened in the story if Mr. Parkenstacker had not adopted a pretense in his conversation with the girl?

____

____

____

____

3. What might have happened in the story if the girl had not acted in such a pretentious manner with Mr. Parkenstacker?

____

____

____

3 **Which Word Does Not Fit?** Choose the word in each row which does *not* fit with the other words and write it on the line.

1. argue	bicker	dispute	question	wrangle	________
2. glaring	insignificant	petty	puny	trivial	________
3. Borneo	Guam	Sahara	Tahiti	Tasmania	________
4. hangman	rascal	rogue	scoundrel	villain	________
5. evident	idealistic	obvious	straightforward	unmistakable	________
6. Dover	Milwaukee	Montreal	Oakland	Pittsburgh	________
7. admiration	approval	fascination	regard	respect	________
8. humble	lowly	meek	modest	self-seeking	________
9. colt	cub	nomad	owlet	puppy	________
10. pretentious	showy	splashy	swank	stately	________
11. flicker	flutter	hover	soar	waver	________
12. doubting	skeptical	uncertain	unconvinced	unsuspecting	________
13. ballet	Charleston	polka	tango	waltz	________
14. impel	incite	motivate	spur	suggest	________
15. boredom	dullness	monotony	routine	stillness	________
16. Adolph	Ehrich	Henri	Pierre	Wilhelmina	________

4 **More about O. Henry.** For each sentence, fill in the *three* best words from the set at the left to complete the sentence correctly.

cleverly
continually
gradually
modestly
scholarly

1. For several generations now, O. Henry (1862-1910), the author of "While the Auto Waits," has been admired by the reading public for his ______________ written stories despite the fact that ______________ critics have ______________ refused to recognize him as a major American author.

determinedly
eventually
hesitatingly
obviously
originally

2. Named William Sydney Porter at birth, O. Henry came ______________ from North Carolina but ______________ moved to Texas where he ______________ pursued the two lines of his artistic interest—drawing and writing.

humility
majority
necessity
prosperity
quantity

3. The ______________ of earning a living led him finally to take a position as teller at the First National Bank in Austin where he spent the ______________ of his working hours drawing, writing, and—in a desperate effort to improve the ______________ of a newspaper he was running on the side—embezzling.

attractive
impressive
objective
offensive
subjective

4. To this day, admirers of O. Henry try to come up with ______________ evidence that proves their idol could never have committed such a(n) ______________ crime; but the judge at the trial would have probably declared such evidence highly ______________, for he sentenced O. Henry to jail.

bearable
reasonable
unbearable
unmistakable
valuable

5. Although he found prison life ______________, the three years he spent in the Ohio Penitentiary were nonetheless ______________ in that it was as Prisoner Number 30664 that he developed the ______________ style that would earn him success as a writer.

abbreviation
assumption
confirmation
opposition
variation

6. No ______________ of this idea exists but one ______________ is that O. Henry, William Sydney Porter's pen name, is a(n) ______________ for the name of a French pharmacist which he had come upon in a reference book while working in the prison pharmacy.

expectation
indication
limitation
objection
quotation

7. One ______________ that as a self-educated writer O. Henry felt a sense of ______________ from his lack of formal schooling is a(n) ______________ from a biography of his life: "I'd give my eyes for a formal education."

boundless
changeless
cheerless
countless
defenseless

8. In 1901 O. Henry stepped forth from the ______________ walls of the Ohio Penitentiary and into the bustling twentieth century. After living briefly with his daughter Margaret in Pittsburgh, he moved to New York City where his writing energy seemed ______________, for he managed to produce ______________ stories for different magazines in a remarkably short period of time.

accompaniment
bewilderment
bombardment
enrichment
fulfillment

9. Managing money continued to be a source of ______________ for O. Henry, whose ______________ of a dream as a successful author was darkened by the ______________ of the creditors who were forever hounding him to pay his many debts.

attraction
observation
proportion
relations
separation

10. Many students of O. Henry's stories share the ______________ that his plots, whether they deal with business, marriage, or social ______________, describe escapes from reality—escapes with which he was sympathetic; for O. Henry suffered from a painful sense of ______________ from the world in which he lived.

5 **Pretenses in the Park.** Match the people listed below with the statements they might make if, like the characters in "While the Auto Waits," their park bench conversations were completely pretentious. The first one has been done to get you started.

alarmist	immigrant	Scrooge
braggart	manipulator	skeptic
escapist	quibbler	✓wallflower

wallflower 1. "Being popular is such a nuisance, isn't it? You just never have a moment to call your own!"

_______________ 2. "Don't you think people should confront their problems rather than running from them the minute the least little thing goes wrong?"

_______________ 3. "This country is getting too crowded. I think people should live in the country in which they were born."

_______________ 4. "I can't stand these doubting Thomases who can never accept anything—and I mean anything—at face value."

_______________ 5. "I have better things to do with my time than have a nervous breakdown every time the six o'clock news brings the latest world crisis into my living room."

_______________ 6. "If people would be a lot more interested in giving and a lot less interested in receiving, this world would be a much better place."

_______________ 7. "Some people—the minute they meet someone—try to figure out how to use them. But not me—I think people should be respected."

_______________ 8. "When you ask me what I think is the most valuable trait a person can have, the first thing that comes to my mind is modesty."

_______________ 9. "You know, if you waste your time quarreling over every little dispute that arises during the course of the day, before you know it your life is nothing but one long argument."

Review: Lessons 1-5

1 **Definitions.** Match the words listed below with the correct definitions.

assumption	fiction	modesty	prosperity
economy	illusion	neutrality	status
excerpt	leisure	organism	technique
feat	luxury	penalty	trivia

_______________ 1. any living individual; any plant or animal

_______________ 2. anything that adds physical comfort; the enjoyment of riches

_______________ 3. freedom from time-consuming duties, or activities; rest

_______________ 4. insignificant matters

_______________ 5. social standing; the legal condition of a person or thing

_______________ 6. the condition of having good fortune or financial success

_______________ 7. the systematic procedure by which any task is accomplished

_______________ 8. the state or policy of not actively taking sides in a matter under dispute

_______________ 9. a passage or scene selected from a speech, book, film, play, or the like

_______________ 10. a statement accepted or supposed true without proof or demonstration

_______________ 11. any act or deed of skill, courage, imagination, or strength; an achievement

_______________ 12. the state or quality of showing a reasonable regard for one's own talents, ability, and value

_______________ 13. the careful or thrifty use or management of resources, such as of income, materials, or labor

_______________ 14. an incorrect perception of reality; the state or condition of being deceived by such perceptions or beliefs

_______________ 15. an event, statement, or occurrence that has been invented or pretended rather than having actually taken place

_______________ 16. a punishment established by law or authority for a crime or offense; the disadvantage or painful consequences resulting from such an action

2 **Word Review.** Fill in the blanks with the set of words that makes the best sense in each sentence.

1. Many people in the audience squirmed uncomfortably in their seats as the ______________ recited ______________ examples of how the typical American household abuses our natural resources.
   (a) archaeologist — obvious
   (b) ecologist — glaring
   (c) etymologist — impressive
   (d) geologist — distinguished

2. The ______________ was ______________ calm considering that his boss had just informed him he was fired and told him to clear out of the building.
   (a) executive — remarkably
   (b) immigrant — continually
   (c) manufacturer — occasionally
   (d) applicant — amazingly

3. Even though he was known to be ______________ to public criticism, Beatrice wrote a letter to the mayor in which she sharply accused him of political ______________.
   (a) immune — favoritism
   (b) hardened — heroism
   (c) attached — idealism
   (d) addicted — cynicism

4. ______________ is the capital of ______________.
   (a) Charleston — South Carolina
   (b) Milwaukee — Wisconsin
   (c) Montreal — Canada
   (d) Pierre — South Dakota

5. David was such a(n) ______________ that he thought conversations about the latest fad were ______________.
   (a) conformist — unfashionable
   (b) illusionist — unsuccessful
   (c) materialist — unsettling
   (d) nonconformist — unbearable

6. Usually, a(n) ______________ has read many books or articles about ______________.
   (a) ambassador — patriotism
   (b) minister — theology
   (c) dramatist — marionettes
   (d) designer — tattoos

7. Not sure that he was using a word ______________, Arthur checked the ______________ in his abridged dictionary.
   (a) accurately — entry
   (b) effectively — aspect
   (c) precisely — quotation
   (d) reasonably — verb

8. "The ______________ maintain(s) that we don't have a chance of winning this election," stated the candidate. "______________, we will continue our campaign efforts."
(a) critics — Whereupon
(b) cynics — Thereafter
(c) media — Furthermore
(d) opposition — Nonetheless

9. ______________ is the study of ______________.
(a) Anthropology — ancient ruins
(b) Biology — organisms
(c) Geology — environmental waste
(d) Sociology — primitive cultures

10. A Greek dramatist once defined the ______________ human being as a person who would always be in the right by ______________.
(a) ideal — instinct
(b) modest — luxury
(c) motivated — leisure
(d) rugged — escapism

3 **Synonyms and Antonyms.** Choose a synonym to fill in the first blank in each sentence. Choose an antonym to fill in the second blank. The first one has been done to get you started.

Synonyms		Antonyms	
cheerless	✓plentiful	actual	necessity
confined	reproduce	boastfully	originate
frill	significant	boundless	pretentious
imaginary	skepticism	conviction	✓scarce
meekly	unbiased	dishonorable	subjective
modest	upright	lighthearted	uneventful

1. Ample and plentiful are antonyms for scarce.
2. Doubt and ________________ are antonyms for ________________.
3. Fictional and ________________ are antonyms for ________________.
4. Glum and ________________ are antonyms for ________________.
5. Humbly and ________________ are antonyms for ________________.
6. Imitate and ________________ are antonyms for ________________.
7. Limited and ________________ are antonyms for ________________.
8. Luxury and ________________ are antonyms for ________________.
9. Meek and ________________ are antonyms for ________________.
10. Moral and ________________ are antonyms for ________________.
11. Noteworthy and ________________ are antonyms for ________________.
12. Objective and ________________ are antonyms for ________________.

4 **Faraway Places.** The places at the left have all been mentioned in the readings in this unit. With the help of a dictionary or encyclopedia, match these faraway places with the correct descriptions.

Australia
Budapest
Fiji
Guam
Hawaii
New Guinea
Sahara
Tahiti
Tasmania
Vietnam

________________ 1. A U.S. air and naval base is located on this Pacific island which is also a territory belonging to the United States.

________________ 2. A tropical country in Southeast Asia, it was here that the longest conflict (1957-1975) in which the United States has ever taken part occurred.

________________ 3. Although much of this city was destroyed during World War II, it is a thriving eastern European capital today.

________________ 4. Captain Cook named these the Sandwich Islands in 1778. Near the middle of the Pacific Ocean, this is the only state in the United States that does not lie on the mainland of North America.

________________ 5. Comprised of about 250 scattered islands, this South Pacific country gained its independence from England in 1970. Its capital, Suva, is located on the largest island.

________________ 6. Extending from the Atlantic Ocean to the Red Sea, this desert, whose name comes from the Arabic word for *desert*, covers about 3½ million square miles, an area roughly equal to that of the United States.

________________ 7. South of the equator, this faraway place is the sixth largest country and the smallest continent in the world.

________________ 8. Surrounded by a broken coral reef, this is the largest island of the Society Islands and is famous for its beauty.

________________ 9. Located north of Australia, this is the second largest island in the world.

________________ 10. This small island state of the Australian Commonwealth is a favorite vacation spot for Australians.

5 **A Final Word on Appearances.** Read this well-known poem and then answer the questions which follow.

The Blind Men and the Elephant

by John Godfrey Saxe

It was six men of Indostan
To learning much inclined,
Who went to see the Elephant
(Though all of them were blind),
That each by observation
Might satisfy his mind.

The First approached the Elephant,
And happening to fall
Against his broad and sturdy side,
At once began to bawl:
"God bless me! but the Elephant
Is very like a wall!"

The Second, feeling of the tusk
Cried, "Ho! what have we here
So very round and smooth and sharp?
To me 'tis very clear
This wonder of an Elephant
Is very like a spear!"

The Third approached the animal
And happening to take
The squirming trunk within his hands
Thus boldly up he spake:
"I see," quoth he, "the Elephant
Is very like a snake!"

The Fourth reached out an eager hand,
And felt about the knee:
"What most this wondrous beast is like
Is very plain," quoth he;
"'Tis clear enough the Elephant
Is very like a tree!"

The Fifth, who chanced to touch the ear,
Said: "E'en the blindest man
Can tell what this resembles most;
Deny the fact who can
This marvel of an Elephant
Is very like a fan!"

The Sixth no sooner had begun
About the beast to grope
Than, seizing on the swinging tail
That fell within his scope,
"I see," quoth he, "the Elephant
Is very like a rope!"

And so these men of Indostan
Disputed loud and long
Each in his own opinion
Exceeding stiff and strong.
Though each was partly in the right,
They all were in the wrong!

1. What illusion does each of the blind men have about his ability to know what an elephant is like?

____

____

____

2. What is the reason that the blind men "disputed loud and long"?

____

____

____

3. Would the blind men agree with the last two lines of the poem? Include reasons which support your answer.

____

____

____

4. What message about reality is offered to us in this poem?

____

____

____

Unit 2

Time

The theme of this unit is *time*. In the five reading selections in this unit, you will have the opportunity to consider the events and ideas relating to the three aspects of time—the past, the present, and the future.

The reading for Lesson 6 is entitled simply "Time." This reading examines how different cultures in different periods of history have viewed time.

"Once upon a Time...," the reading for Lesson 7, deals with the distant past. This reading selection presents information about one symbol of the distant past that continues to be a source of lively interest and debate—the dinosaur.

One time-related concern that more and more of us in our own American culture are becoming aware of is the fact that people are living longer. In "How to Live to Be 100 or More," the reading for Lesson 8, the entertainer George Burns offers some tips on how to live to a ripe old age.

The reading for Lesson 9 is entitled "What Will the Future Bring?" The author of this selection presents some of the methods people throughout history have used to predict the future.

One type of reading that specializes in thoughts about the future is science fiction. In the short story, "All Summer in a Day," the selection for Lesson 10, author Ray Bradbury portrays a day in the life of an American girl on another planet.

Lesson 6

Time

Words for Study

inhabit	disruption	essential	siesta
intricately	anniversaries	duration	ventures
instinctive	bar mitzvah	Mohammedanism	vital
continuity	migrations	U.S.S.R.	infinite

Time

Throughout all of our experience, through every aspect of the world and universe we inhabit, runs that mysterious something called time. The clock, deputy for the sun and stars, tells us it is time to get up, time to go to school or to work, time to put the roast in the oven or to eat it, time to retire. Setting out on a journey, we check timetables of train or plane against our watches; putting out to sea, we must relate time to distance in order to find our way.

Time governs not merely our activities but our very being. Like every living organism, we exist by grace of thousands of intricately timed rhythms. Our pulses keep time, peacefully or otherwise; the electrical waves in our brains time their rhythms to sleep or wakefulness.

Other living creatures, far more than human beings, are governed by "biological time" that links inner processes to the regular rhythms of the outside world. The morning glory opens by the clock; the maple leaf grows green or flames scarlet by the calendar; the mallard flies north or south—taking its direction from some instinctive inner calculation involving time and the sun.

Time, which gives continuity and pattern to life, also brings disruption and death. The morning glory, splendid in the dawn, is wilted at noon; man, maple, and mallard live their appointed span. The eternal hills were not there a hundred million years ago and will be gone a hundred million years hence. Even the stars shift with the centuries and, early or late, must eventually fade out. There is nothing under the sun, or over it, of which we cannot say: "This, too—in time—will pass away."

To any person, the most important single unit of time is that of his own stay on earth. Each of us marks off our personal life span in personal terms, by the major events that happen only once. Birth, marriage, the arrival of children make milestones which we remember and celebrate with birthdays and anniversaries. Our acceptance into adult society may be noted by confirmation, bar mitzvah, graduation from school or, in more primitive societies, by tests of strength and skill.

Time is a great teacher, a great healer, a great leveler; it stands still, slips away from us, or flies past us. We can save time or lose it, spend time or waste it (time is money!), even beat it or kill it.

What we cannot do, oddly enough, is define it. To the psychologist, time is the means by which we give order to our experiences. To the physicist, time is one of the three fundamental quantities in terms of which he can describe anything in the universe. (The other two are mass and distance.) To the philosopher, time is still other things. Yet these learned men, though they may write books about time, cannot define it in a satisfactory way to each other, or even to themselves.

Divisions of time have been defined, however, and their history is an interesting one. It was the Egyptians who gave us the 365-day year. Late spring in the Valley of the Nile was the time when Egyptians gazed skyward and waited for the important flood that would water their crops. With this event, the Egyptians started their new year. Many centuries were to pass, however, before the calendar year as we know it today was to be established and accepted. People didn't always react calmly to new adjustments in the calendar, either.

In 1752, for example, England and its colonies finally decided to conform to the calendar used in Catholic Europe. What this meant was that eleven days had to be cut from the English calendar. This event touched off riots in England where many people, angry because they had been cheated out of eleven days' rent money, rioted to the cry, "Give us back our eleven days." In America, the colonist Ben Franklin advised a more philosophic view, telling his readers not to regret the loss of so much time but rather to rejoice that one might "lie down in Peace on the second of this month and not awake till the morning of the 14th."

The seasons of the year have always governed people's lives and in turn have been adopted as basic units of time. The seasons help us gain our food, telling us when to hunt animals and plant crops. Modern industry depends on seasonal movements of goods; clothes, cars, air conditioners, even toys—are all made and sold according to seasonal needs.

Some societies are ruled by the seasons. Laplanders follow the seasonal migrations of the reindeer. The nomadic tribes of Iran and Afghanistan uproot themselves from the valleys in the spring to seek the rich grasslands in the mountains. In the cold weather, they return to the valleys. To these people, shuttling between mountain and valley, time is broken in two by the seasons.

The month, like the seasons, was given to man by nature. Its origin rests in the length of time—about 29 days—it takes for the moon to orbit the earth. For many people, the moon has long been an object of wonder and worship. In Asia, for example, the moon governs some Buddhist religious observations. In the West, however, the month is less strictly measured by the movements of the moon and has become a time unit of convenience, a useful way to subdivide the year and the seasons. One of the chief functions of the month is as a time unit of business. Bills, rent, and credit payments are usually due each month. For many people, payday is a monthly event.

Every society has had to invent the week, for a time unit smaller than a month but longer than a day is essential to human affairs. A community functions more smoothly if regularly recurring days are set aside for laundry, marketing, time off from the job, and worship.

The ancient Greeks split their months into three 10-day weeks and the Romans had a market week of eight days ending with a day of rest and festivals. Among primitive tribes today, the market week varies in duration from four to ten days. Oddly enough, the seven-day week is practically unknown among these societies—it is the one week-length not in use by them.

Among the major nations of the world, however, the seven-day week is the custom. This length was derived from Genesis—"And on the seventh day, God rested"—and was established over most of the world by the spread of Christianity and Mohammedanism. Attempts to change the seven-day week in Western society have always failed. In our own century, for example, the U.S.S.R. tried twice to alter the week, decreeing a week of five days in 1929 and a week of six days in 1932. But by 1940, the seven-day week had been restored.

Since man first walked the earth, the day has been the most obvious indicator of time's passage. Nothing exerts a greater control on our sense of time and activity than the blaze of light and warmth that floods the world at dawn, and the cool darkness that occurs when the sun sets.

With each sunrise, our work begins—planting fields, selling our wares, toiling in factory or office. As the sun crosses the sky, the tempo of the day increases; as the sun begins to set, our working hours come slowly to a halt. Farm animals are bedded down, shops are closed, and it is time for family, food, and relaxation. Soon the dark side of the earth is falling asleep, with only our own artificial lights left to take the place of the departed sun—while half the globe away the sun is just rising and people are stirring as they make ready to begin their daily routine.

The hour is an invention of Western civilization, and it dictates an entire way of life. The hour tells us when to start work and when to quit, when to sleep and when to rise. People once ate whenever they were hungry, but today mealtimes are often fixed to an hour.

Today, the hours are such regulators of life that it is hard to think of a day without them. Yet the hour only gained importance in the 14th century when European towns mounted mechanical clocks that chimed out the time 24 hours a day. Before that, the day had been divided less accurately.

As exact as hours can make time, not every society uses them in the same way. In the United States, for example, the office day generally occupies the hours between about 9 a.m. and 5 p.m. In Spain, office workers report at about 9, but take a four-hour break at 1 for dinner and siesta, then return to work at 5 and leave at 8. Spaniards sit down for a light supper around 11 p.m. about the hour most Americans are falling asleep.

The first clocks had no minute hands; in fact, the minute only gained importance with the development of modern societies. During the Industrial Revolution, which began in the mid-18th century, trains began to run on schedules, factory whistles blew to change shifts, the tempo of life quickened, and the minute became a major governing unit of time.

Even the minute is too long for modern science. In the ventures of man into space, with all the intricate calculations involved, the second, millisecond and microsecond now stand as the vital measures of time.

It is hard for most people to imagine why anyone would *want* to measure time in millionths of a second (microseconds). In our daily affairs—taking a cake out of the oven, getting to school, catching the morning train—our clocks and watches serve us well if they are correct to within a minute or two. Even so specialized an activity as timing a footrace requires a stopwatch accurate only to tenths of a second.

Yet almost everyone relies, directly or indirectly, on extremely precise time measurements. They are essential to the distribution of electric power; the utility engineer, synchronizing the output of tens or hundreds of generators, needs a master clock correct to a few tens of microseconds. Without precise time measurement, modern science could not exist. The physicist studying the pieces of atoms produced by an atom smasher deals in particles that appear and disappear in nanoseconds (1/1,000 of a microsecond); to make sense out of his experiments, he must be able to determine the time sequence of these fleeting events with split-microsecond precision.

Time, which is everywhere yet nowhere, which seems obvious yet cannot be defined by logic, has fascinated questioning minds in almost every age. Is time real or unreal? Does it move in one direction only, or can it be reversed? Does it have a beginning or an end, or is it infinite? None of these questions has yet been answered to everyone's satisfaction. Yet the mere asking of them stretches the mind, and the search for answers, though it may prove unsuccessful, can still tell us much about time and the universe in which we live.

---

1 **Understanding the Reading.** Put the letter of the best answer on the line at the left.

_____ 1. Which unit of time was *not* the invention of mankind?

(a) second (b) minute (c) hour (d) day

_____ 2. Which of the following is *not* an example of the moon's influence on different cultures?

(a) a source of wonderment
(b) a time for paying bills
(c) religious observances
(d) the duration of a month

_____ 3. Which of the following is *least* governed by "biological time"?

(a) mallards (b) maples (c) mankind (d) morning glories

_____ 4. For most people, the most important period of time is _____.

(a) a week (b) a month (c) a year (d) their life span

_____ 5. The hour first became an important time unit in the _____.

(a) 1300s (b) 1400s (c) 1500s (d) 1600s

_____ 6. The minute became an important concept _____.

(a) before the concept of an hour became important
(b) as people found it necessary to follow more exact schedules
(c) during the twentieth century
(d) when people discovered they needed a unit of time larger than a second but smaller than an hour

_____ 7. The week probably does not have a universally common definition because _____.

(a) months vary in length
(b) the number of hours of daylight varies with the seasons
(c) the concept of week is not found on most timepieces
(d) the concept of week is not as closely tied to natural or scientific phenomena as many other units of time

_____ 8. The authors cite the example of the Spaniards to demonstrate that _____.

(a) Americans organize their work time more effectively
(b) siestas are a feature of "biological time" in a hot climate
(c) different cultures define the length of the work day differently
(d) the hour is a time unit used only by Western cultures

_____ 9. As time has passed, people have found it necessary to _____.

(a) measure time more accurately
(b) define time using logic
(c) redefine the length of an hour
(d) pay more attention to how the moon influences the seasons

_____ 10. The authors contend that mankind _____.

(a) still has much to learn before time can be accurately defined
(b) believes that time cannot be reversed
(c) does not require precise time measurements in order to function well
(d) will probably need to revise the calendar again at some future date

2 **What Do You Think?** In the reading, the authors cite many ways in which we regard time. In good sentence form, give a personal example of each of the following.

1. Saving time: ______________________________

____

2. Losing time: ______________________________

____

3. Killing time: ______________________________

____

4. Time flying: ______________________________

____

5. Time standing still: ______________________________

____

3 **Durations.** Use context clues and some intelligent guessing to complete these statements about durations with the words listed below.

aspirin	Easter	male	Pluto	tadpole
blood	female	*Mayflower*	senator	*Titanic*
bullfrog	fingernail	Mercury	snail	whale
Chicago	gopher	Philadelphia	snowflake	wrens

1. It takes 10 minutes for a ________________ to form.
2. ________________ takes two hours to reach its peak effectiveness in the human body.
3. It took four hours for the ________________ to sink after ramming an iceberg on April 15, 1912.
4. It takes 9 hours, 45 minutes to travel from ________________ to Memphis by rail.
5. It takes 24 hours for a mother ________________ to produce 200 quarts of milk.
6. A pair of ________________ feed their young 1,117 times in 24 hours.
7. In colonial times, a stagecoach ride from Manhattan to ________________ took three days.
8. It took the Pilgrims 55 days to cross the Atlantic aboard the ________________.
9. It takes 87.96 days for ________________ to revolve around the sun.
10. It takes 248.4 years for ________________ to revolve around the sun.
11. It takes 117 days for the body to replace a lost ________________.
12. The life span of human ________________ cells is 120 days.
13. The teeth of a ________________ grow as much as 40 inches in one year.
14. It takes 15 months for a ________________ to grow into a ________________.
15. Six years is the life span of a ________________ and the term of a U.S. ________________.
16. 22.47 years is the lifetime sleep requirement for the average American ________________;

    25 years, 25 days is the lifetime sleep requirement for the average American ________________.
17. It takes 95 years for ________________ to recur on the same date.

---

4 **Origins of Calendar Words.** This exercise deals with calendar words which come from Roman and Norse mythology. For each group of sentences, fill in the blanks with the *three* best words from the set at the left.

incomparable
inconsistent
inconvenient
indefinite
indisputable

1. **March** was the first month of the year according to the ancient Roman calendar which contained only ten months. Beginning the new year in the spring is ________________ with the calendar we use, but the Romans started the new year in the spring because it was the beginning of the planting season. It is an ________________ fact that the very early Italians worshipped Mars as the god of agriculture, and they dedicated the coming of spring to him and to the ________________ blessings of planting and rebirth.

readjusted
reassured
reestablished
reinforced
represented

2. **January** was named after the Roman god Janus, the god of beginnings and of doors and gateways. Janus was ________________ as having two faces so that he might guard both entrances and exits. This has ________________ the mistaken belief that January was so named because it was the first month of the year. In fact, however, when the ten-month Roman calendar was ________________ about 700 B.C., January was added as the eleventh month and so named because it contained a feast day in honor of Janus.

denoted
denounce
deprived
derived
desist

3. **February** is ________________ from the Latin *februo* which means "to purify." February 15th ________________ an important festival for the Romans. On this day priests ran through the streets, touching or striking everyone they met with strips of skin from sacrificed goats. Women prayed that the priests would not ________________ from this activity until they had been touched or struck, for the goat skins were thought to be charms against childlessness.

encouraged
encrust
endorse
ensnared
envisioned

4. **Saturday** was named after the planet Saturn. The ancient Egyptians had ________________ a seven-day week and named the days after the seven planets known to them. The Romans adopted this system around A.D. 300 and later ________________ the people of northern Europe to ________________ it also.

discredit
disfigured
disorganized
disorder
distant

5. **Wednesday** was named in honor of Odin, or Woden, chief among the Scandinavian gods, who created heaven and earth out of ________________ and who ruled from his ________________ throne in Valhalla. Odin's face was ________________ for he had sacrificed an eye in striving to attain wisdom.

misconception
misfortunes
misgivings
misled
mismanaged

6. **Friday** was probably named after Odin's wife, Frigga, who presided over marriages and knew the fate of all people. Some etymologists, however, have ________________ about this theory. These etymologists believe that Friday was named after the Norse goddess of love, Freya. This is probably a ________________. With the similarity in the two names, it is easy to see how one group of etymologists was ________________.

exceptional
exceptionally
exertions
expectations
expressive

7. **Thursday** was named to honor Thor, the son of Odin and Frigga. Thor was believed to have ________________ strength. He was the god of agriculture and the friend of man, whom he aided and guarded against evil spirits and disease. His ________________ on behalf of mankind made him an ________________ popular god.

undoubtedly
ungodly
unfortunate
uninjured
unparalleled

8. **Tuesday** was named in honor of Tyr, another son of Odin. Tyr's bravery among the Norse gods was ________________. As his father had lost an eye to gain knowledge, the ________________ Tyr lost a hand while fighting a wolf who had made the ________________ vow to destroy Valhalla where Odin's throne was located. Old English mythology gave him the name of Tiw, and the day which honored him was *Tiwesdoeg*.

---

5 **The Flower Clock.** In the formal gardens of 19th century Europe, flower clocks provided a clever and beautiful way of telling time. A flower clock consisted of several flower beds arranged to form the face of a clock. There was a separate bed for each hour of the day. Each bed contained a type of flower that either opened or closed during that hour. When the sun was shining, a flower clock could be used to tell time within half an hour.

Based on the diagram of a sample flower clock below, answer the questions which follow in good sentence form. Be sure to include an explanation in your response. The first one has been done to get you started.

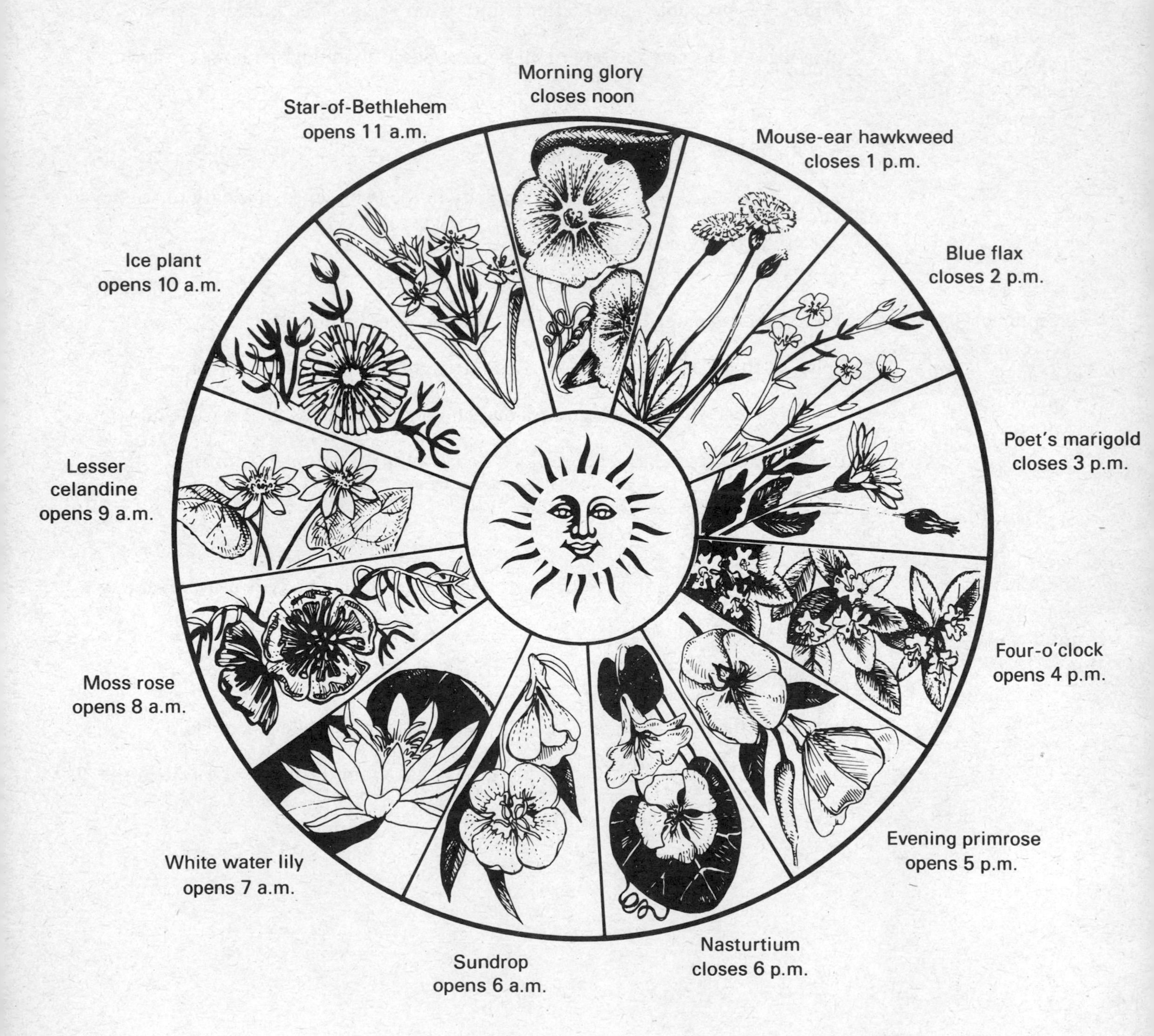

Which flower bed would you look at if you wanted to determine:

1. whether or not you had overslept? I would look at the sundrop, because I need to get up at 6:00 a.m.

2. whether or not you were late for work or school? ______________________

3. whether or not it was almost time for lunch? ______________________

4. whether or not you still had time to make it to the post office? ______________________

5. whether or not the local TV news program had begun? ______________________

Lesson 7

Once upon a Time...

Words for Study

stagnant	mammoths	extinct	sociable
Gobi	posterity	Mesozoic	submerged
dinosaurs	scavengers	vertebrae	estimated
perished	mobile	cathedral	efficient

Once upon a Time...

During the immense span of time since life began, many things have changed. The positions of rivers and mountains and the very outlines of continents have altered. Plant life and animal life have changed so much that, if we were snatched back to a former geological era, we might think we had landed on another planet.

Much of our knowledge of this strange and remote past is gained from the study of fossils. The word *fossil* was first used by a 16th century German physician, Georgius Agricola, who wrote about the earth and its products. Agricola used the word *fossil*, from the Latin *fossum* which meant *dug*, to indicate anything dug out of the earth. Gradually, the word came to be limited to objects found in the earth or its rocks that were the remains of living things.

For a living thing to become a fossil, it must be buried soon after its death so that oxygen and oxygen-breathing organisms cannot reach it. On land, such burials may take place in quicksands, bogs, swamps, and small, stagnant bodies of water. Although some animals are fossilized after they have drifted about in the waters of rivers and lakes, such animals are less likely to be preserved whole.

In dry regions, sandstorms often bury and preserve animals. In the Gobi Desert in Central Asia, for example, whole herds of dinosaurs and early mammals perished in this fashion and have been recovered only recently by a Polish woman scientist. One of the world's richest fossil deposits has been found in the tar pits of Rancho La Brea in Los Angeles. Mammoths, saber-toothed cats, camels, horses, and other inhabitants of long ago were trapped in tar, and their fossils have filled out many museum collections throughout the United States.

Despite the various ways that fossils may be created, only an extremely small fraction of all the billions of ancient plants and animals have had the good fortune to be preserved for posterity. When most living things die, swarms of scavengers, from invisible bacteria up to crabs, hyenas and vultures, descend upon them and swiftly consume them.

Few indeed are the plants and animals that have left recognizable remains; fewer still have had the luck to be found by fossil-hunters. Many fossils may lie in their rocks for millions of years, only to be mashed out of shape by the stresses in the earth's mobile crust. Therefore, the fossils that men and women have recovered do not give a complete or even balanced picture of ancient life. Nevertheless, the information they do provide is valuable in helping scientists to reconstruct the distant past.

Perhaps the fossils that have continued to fascinate us the most are those of animals that lived 140 million years ago which were quite unlike any living thing on earth today—the dinosaurs. Dinosaurs were reptiles, now extinct, that lived during the Mesozoic Era of earth history, a time span that began about 225 million years ago and ended some 65 million years ago. The duration of the dinosaurs during this geological era was about 35 million years.

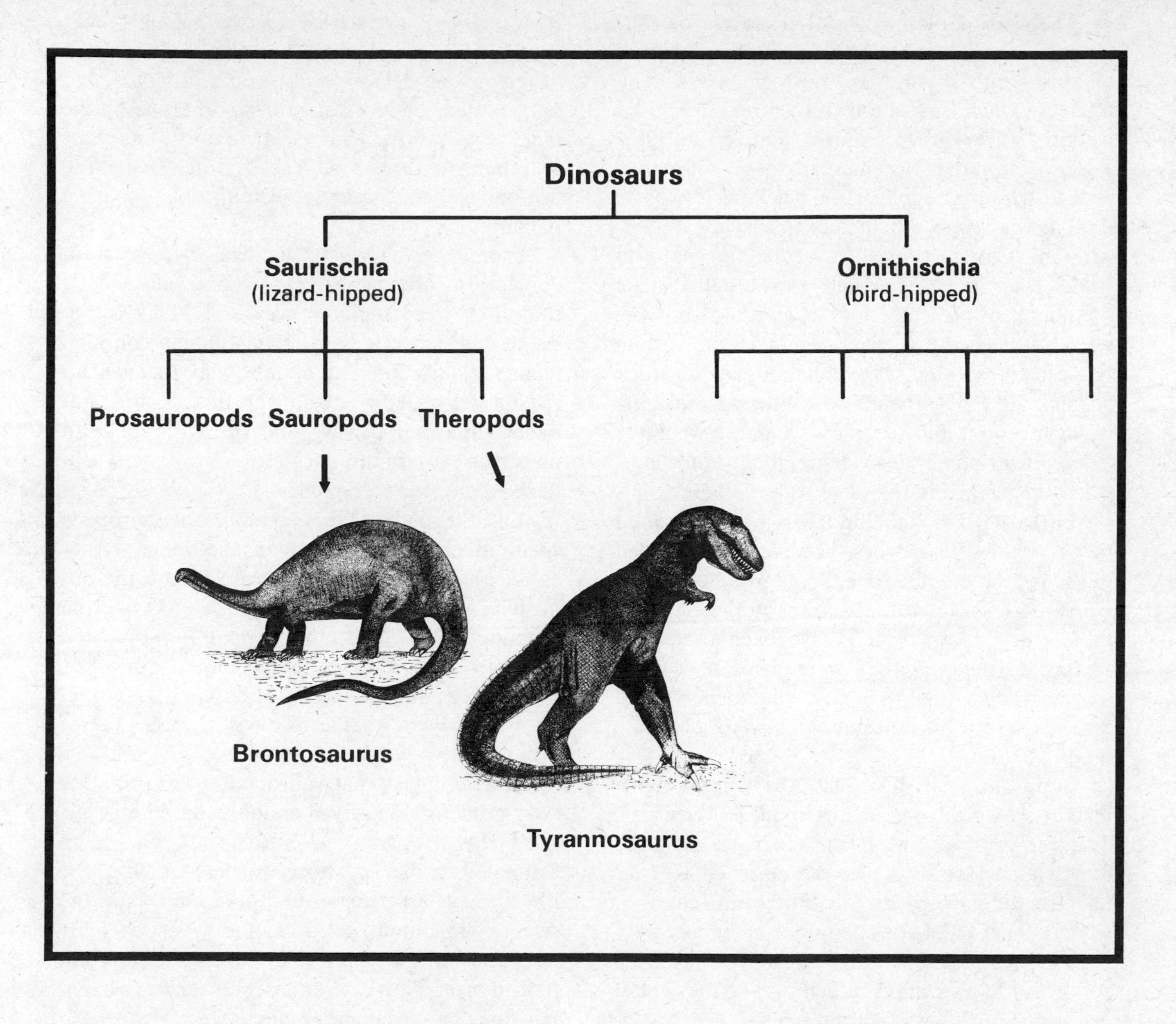

These heroes of the Age of Reptiles are not really one order, but two, which evolved separately from common ancestors. In science, an *order* refers to a category of animals or plants. The two orders of dinosaurs are the Saurischia (sor-IS-ke-a) or lizard-hipped, and the Ornithischia (or-nith-IS-ke-a) or bird-hipped. The Saurischia order includes two of the best-known dinosaurs: the long-necked, small-headed, plant-eaters, like Brontosaurus (bront-ta-SOR-us) and the short-necked, big-headed, two-legged flesh-eaters like Tyrannosaurus (te-ran-a-SOR-us). The smaller relatives of both these dinosaurs are included in this order. All other dinosaurs are classified in the Ornithischia order.

The sauropods (SOR-o-pods), plant-eating dinosaurs which belong to the Saurishcia order, are the big ones—the animals that people first think of when they hear the word *dinosaur*. Sauropods were the largest land animals of all time. They were a living answer to the question: How big can a land animal get?

A typical sauropod, like Brontosaurus, was a beast about 60 feet long, standing 15 to 18 feet high at the highest point along its back, over its hips. It weighed something like 25 to 35 tons. Compare this incredible size with the cow Indian elephants that one sees in zoos and circuses which weigh two or three tons.

The sauropod supported this weight on four massive legs. The hind legs, which carried most of the weight, were especially massive. The forelegs, which carried only a fraction of the total weight, were shorter, more slender, and less straight. Brontosaurus and many other sauropods walked with their forelegs slightly bowed.

The feet were designed for carrying weight, with short toes arranged in a spreading pattern. Under each foot was a thick elastic pad to take the shock of footfalls and to give the foot the stretch it needed to keep the animal from getting stuck in soft ground. An elephant is seldom stuck because its foot expands when the animal puts its weight on it and contracts when the weight is taken off. From all the evidence about sauropods, their feet worked in the same way.

Both the fore and hind feet of a sauropod had five toes. These toes, however, were buried in the round, stumpy foot. Some toes bore claws while others did not. Because of the animal's build, these claws would have been useless as weapons. However, they were no doubt useful for moving in shallow water, where they could be hooked into the bottom, and also for climbing muddy banks.

Supporting all this mass was a remarkable backbone, which consisted of about 80 vertebrae. The vertebrae of the neck, the back, and the forward part of the tail were designed to bear terrific loads with an absolute minimum of weight. There was not one ounce of unnecessary bone. The backbone of a sauropod has been compared to a splendid cathedral, like those built in Europe during the Middle Ages.

The head, a little bigger than that of a human being, was amazingly small compared to the rest of the beast. The skull was very light; the jaws were weak; the teeth, peglike or spoon-shaped. The nostrils were set high, so that in the water the animal could breathe without raising much of its head above the surface—a construction found in the crocodile and the hippopotamus today. The brain was only a few inches long and weighed just a few ounces. But then, the brains of all reptiles are very small in comparison with those of birds and mammals of similar size.

Fifty to 75 years ago, when sauropods were first being studied, there was much argument about their posture and habits. Within the last 30 years, however, sauropod trackways from a river in Texas have settled many of the questions. Some dinosaurs walked on land, since their dragging tails left grooves, while others waded up to their bellies. In still another case, the trackways show that a dinosaur was half swimming, with its hind legs floating clear of the bottom and its forelegs reaching down to pole the animal gently along.

From these tracks, we can draw certain conclusions about the life of sauropods. One is that they were sociable creatures. This is not surprising, since a herding instinct is common among plant-eating mammals, and there is no reason why plant-eating reptiles should not behave in a similar way. Modern reptiles mislead us because a large majority are flesh-eaters, and flesh-eaters tend to be loners.

Like the modern hippopotamus, the sauropods spent much of their time in the water, either submerged or wading. However, they came out on land whenever they felt like it and, like the hippopotamus, could move around quite briskly. Like elephants, they probably moved quite fast even when they seemed to be loafing along, because they were able to cover a great deal of ground with a single stride.

We can guess that sauropods were probably slow-growing, long-lived animals. Based on their size, the life span of sauropods has been estimated at one or two centuries, which is the life span of large turtles and crocodiles. Yet, the size of an animal alone is not a very reliable indicator of how long it takes an animal to attain its full size. Thus, it cannot be said for certain how long a dinosaur normally lived.

There is much more certainty about the diet of sauropods, which is obvious from a study of their teeth and general build. They ate soft marsh plants by nipping them off with their blunt teeth. It is sometimes asked how such a small head could possibly gather enough food to keep such a vast mass of muscle fueled. In the first place, with such a long neck, the animal was really an efficient food-gatherer. It could reach so far in all directions that it lost little time in moving about. Secondly, a reptile consumes only a fraction of the food that a mammal or a bird of the same weight does in the same time. Anyone who has observed reptiles at the local zoo knows that they spend a great deal of time lying still and doing nothing. Therefore, a few hundred pounds of marsh plants a day should have been enough to support a sauropod, which spent much of its time just floating in water.

Scientists refer to the dying out of these great reptiles as the Great Death. What exactly happened to the dinosaurs? There are many theories to account for the Great Death. One theory, for example, is that the flesh-eating dinosaurs ate all the other dinosaurs and then starved to death. The objection to this theory is that it does not take into account the death of dinosaurs living in the sea. Why did they die at the same time? Another theory is that a plague destroyed all the dinosaurs. Although disease can greatly reduce the number of a species, it is very rare that an entire species is killed in this way. Still another theory with which most of us are familiar is that an ice age caused the disappearance of the dinosaurs. Yet there is no evidence of a sharp change in climate when dinosaurs walked the earth.

These are only three of the many theories that have been proposed to explain the Great Death. Considered individually, all the theories have serious flaws. More than likely, it was a combination of factors that resulted in the Great Death. We do not know yet *what* that combination of factors was, and this puzzle will probably continue to wrinkle the brows of researchers for many years to come.

Adapted from *The Day of the Dinosaur* by L. Sprague de Camp and Catherine Crook de Camp. Garden City: Doubleday & Company, Inc., 1968. Used by permission.

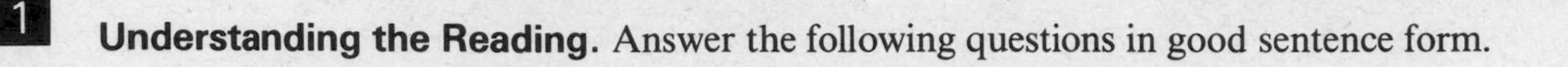

1 **Understanding the Reading.** Answer the following questions in good sentence form.

1. Explain why most organisms do not become fossils.

____

2. Cite two ways in which an organism can become a fossil.

   a. ____

   b. ____

3. Explain how Rancho La Brea in Los Angeles has been helpful to us in understanding more about the distant past.

____

____

____

4. Define *order* as it is used by scientists.

____

5. Which order of dinosaurs do the de Camps describe in detail?

____

6. Cite four features of a sauropod's body and describe how these features helped the sauropod function.

   a. ____

   b. ____

   c. ____

   d. ____

7. Briefly describe the eating habits of a sauropod. How are they similar to those of modern reptiles? How are they different?

____

____

____

____

____

____

8. Cite two theories for the Great Death and the objections that have been raised for each of these theories.

   a. ____

   ____

   ____

   b. ____

   ____

   ____

9. Briefly explain the de Camps' viewpoint regarding the cause for the Great Death.

   ____

   ____

   ____

   ____

2 **Scientific Classification: Part 1.** In the reading, the scientific definition of the word *order* was mentioned. Use the words listed at the left to complete this additional information about scientific classification.

arrange
indicates
method
related
relationships

1. Scientific classification, a ________________ scientists have developed to ________________ all animals and plants in ________________ groups, ________________ certain ________________ among animal groups and among plant groups.

agree
differ
judgment
scheme
specimens

2. Because a particular ________________ is based on opinion and ________________ formed after studying ________________, not all biologists ________________ on how individual animals and plants fit into it, and so classifications often ________________ in details.

common
correct
recognized
scholars
words

3. Latin and Greek ________________ are used in scientific classification because early ________________ used these languages. Although animals or plants are known by different ________________ names, each has only one ________________ scientific name which is ________________ anywhere in the world.

largest
plant
seven
system
two

4. ________________ chief groups make up the ________________ of scientific classification. The ________________ group is the **kingdom.** There are only ________________ kingdoms, the animal kingdom and the ________________ kingdom.

animals
backbones
divided
kingdom
phylum

5. **Phylum** is the second largest group. The animal ________________ may be ________________ into 20 or more phyla. All ________________ with ________________ belong to the ________________ *Chordata.*

characteristics
Chordata
class
members
phylum

6. **Class** members have more ______________ in common than do ______________ of a ______________. For example, mammals, reptiles, and birds all belong to the phylum ______________, but each belongs to a different ______________.

class
flesh
insects
milk
moles

7. **Order** consists of groups that are more alike than those in a ______________. In the class *Mammalia*, all animals produce ______________ for their young. But because such animals as dogs and raccoons eat ______________, they are grouped in the order *Carnivora*, while such animals as ______________ and shrews, which eat ______________, are classified in the order *Insectivora*.

Carnivora
family
Felidae
order
tails

8. **Family** is made up of groups that are even more alike than those in the ______________. For example, wolves and cats are both in the order ______________. But wolves belong to the ______________ *Canidae* because of their long snouts and bushy ______________, while cats, with their short snouts and short-haired tails, belong to the family ______________.

breed
coyote
different
genus
similar

9. **Genus** consists of very ______________ groups, but members of ______________ groups usually cannot ______________ with one another. Both the ______________ and the timber wolf are in the ______________ *Canis*, but they generally don't breed with one another.

basic
forms
genus
one
two

10. **Species** is the ______________ unit of scientific classification. Members of a species have many common characteristics, but they differ from all other ______________ of life in ______________ or more ways. No ______________ species in a ______________ have the same scientific name.

3 **Scientific Classification: Part 2.** The chart below provides a simplified example of classification. Refer to the chart to answer the questions which follow.

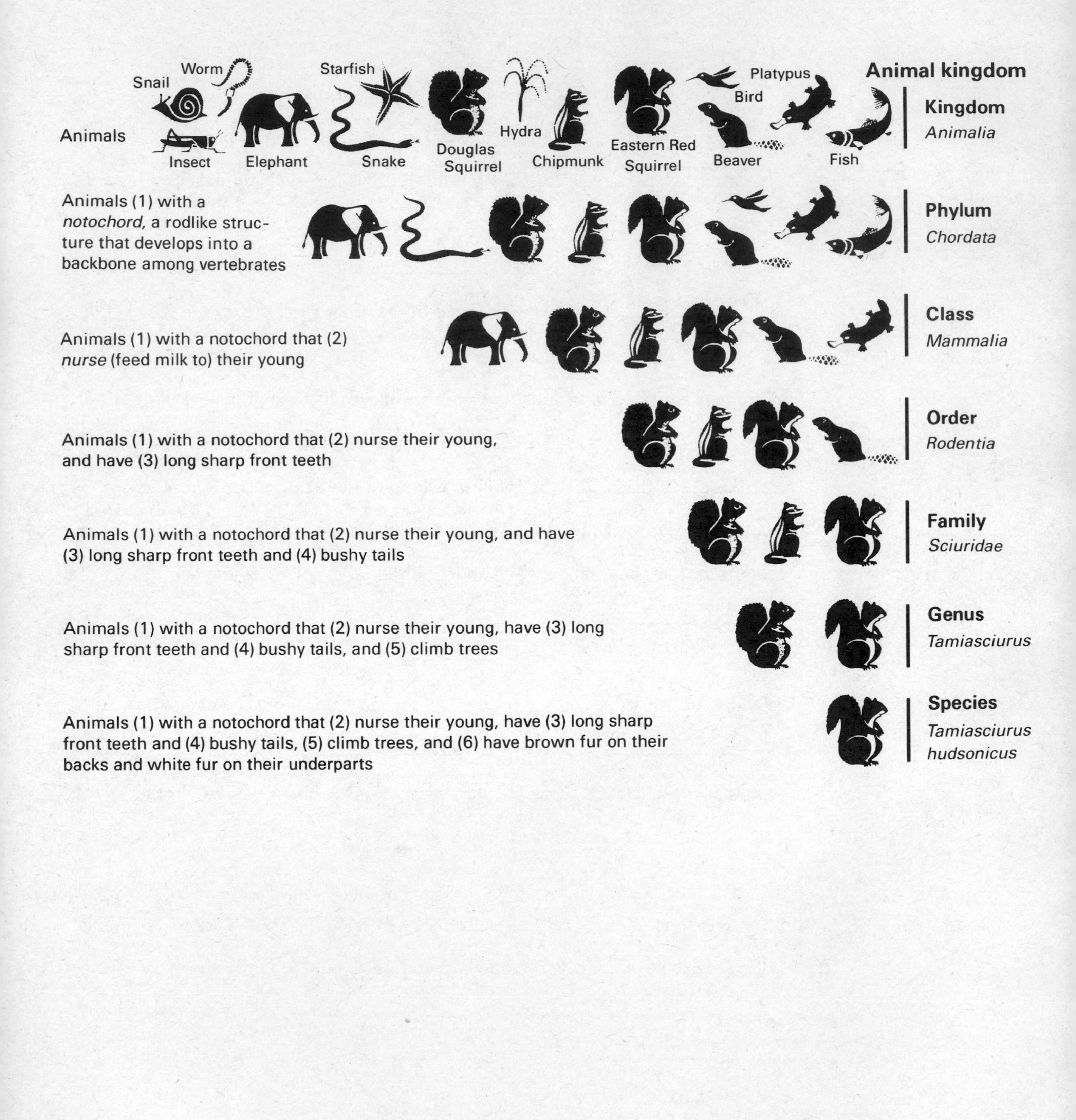

_____ 1. The major purpose of the chart is to show _____.

(a) how an Eastern red squirrel is different from a Douglas squirrel
(b) that scientific classification is a painstaking and difficult process
(c) that the majority of the members of the animal kingdom have backbones
(d) how an Eastern red squirrel can be separated from any other species of animal

_____ 2. Which of the following groupings is incorrect?

(a) Kingdom: beaver, hydra, platypus, snail
(b) Phylum: bird, fish, insect, snake
(c) Class: beaver, Douglas squirrel, elephant, platypus
(d) Order: beaver, chipmunk, Douglas squirrel, Eastern red squirrel

_____ 3. Unlike the beaver, the chipmunk _____.

(a) nurses its young
(b) has a notochord
(c) has a bushy tail
(d) has sharp front teeth

_____ 4. The major difference between a fish and a starfish in scientific classification is that _____.

(a) a fish nurses its young
(b) a fish shares a classification with a hydra
(c) a starfish can live only in salt water
(d) a starfish lacks a notochord

_____ 5. The chart pictures only one member of *Tamiasciurus hudsonicus* because _____.

(a) all other members are extinct
(b) each species has its own name
(c) scientists cannot agree on the other members
(d) there was no more room on the page

4 Putting Events in Order.

Putting Events in Order. Scientists are not the only people concerned with order. Can you arrange these events about fossil hunting in order so that they make sense? The first sentence in each group has been numbered to get you started.

1. ____ At the head of the valley stood a half-ruined cabin.

   ____ Far south of him rose a ridge known as Como Bluff.

   ____ North of the bluff, the land dipped into a shallow valley.

   __1__ One day in 1897, a young man named Walter Granger rode across a plain in southeastern Wyoming.

   ____ The ground around it was littered with rusty-brown boulders.

2. ____ All had come from sandstone that formed the surrounding land.

   __1__ Granger was collecting fossils for the new American Museum of Natural History in New York City.

   ____ He soon saw that the boulders were more than lumps of stone.

   ____ Other bones, not so badly worn, formed the lower walls of the cabin.

   ____ They were battered, weather-beaten bones of big dinosaurs.

3. ____ By that time the Bone Cabin deposit had yielded 483 portions of varied dinosaurs.

   ____ Collecting began the following spring.

   __1__ The collector reported that Bone Cabin contained a rich deposit of dinosaur fossils.

   ____ These specimens formed the greatest collection of fossil reptile remains ever taken from a single locality.

   ____ Work continued through six summers, into the autumn of 1903.

Adapted from *Tales Told by Fossils* by Carroll Lane Fenton. Garden City: Doubleday & Company, Inc., 1966. Used by permission of Doubleday & Company, Inc.

5

A Review of Singular and Plural Words. Most plural words are formed by adding *s* or *es*. Unfortunately, there are exceptions. With the help of a dictionary, write the plural form of each word listed below. If the dictionary gives more than one plural form for a word, write both forms.

1. appendix ______________________
2. child ______________________
3. coyote ______________________
4. crisis ______________________
5. Englishman ______________________
6. hippopotamus ______________________
7. index ______________________
8. knife ______________________
9. mouse ______________________
10. phylum ______________________
11. radius ______________________
12. sister-in-law ______________________
13. series ______________________
14. shelf ______________________
15. species ______________________
16. studio ______________________
17. thief ______________________
18. trout ______________________
19. vertebra ______________________
20. woman ______________________

Lesson 8

How to Live to Be 100 or More

Words for Study

longevity	Bela Lugosi	enthusiasm	Niagara Falls
limber	turbulence	memorabilia	merit
congestion	minimize	tangerines	conscience
chlorine	anesthetic	vigorous	reputation

How to Live to Be 100 or More

In this reading selection, comedian George Burns gives some advice on how to live to be 100. As a person nearing ninety and still working at the time this material was written, he is a good one to give such advice.

* * *

Bettman Archive

Now, you're probably asking why would anyone want to live to be 100. I know some people who are not the least interested in reaching that age, but it so happens they're all under 10. What do they care about growing old? They've got more important things to worry about, like whether the cookies are crisp. Most of the people I know who are still living want to keep living.

I'm a member of the Hillcrest Country Club, and I must run into fifty or sixty people a day. I've yet to meet anybody who said, "George, I'd like to die today." Dying is not popular; it's never caught on. That's understandable; it's bad for the complexion. It also upsets your daily routine and leaves you with too much time on your hands.

I don't know about you, but there are lots of reasons for me to live to be 100 or more. For one thing, I've got all these age jokes and I've got to use them—they're funny. Like when I talk about becoming a country singer and I say, "Why shouldn't I be a country singer? I'm older than most countries." That gets a laugh. Or I'll say, "They had this song, 'I Wish I Was 18 Again,' and they wanted the oldest man around to sing it. But at that time Moses happened to be busy so they asked me." That's another laugh.

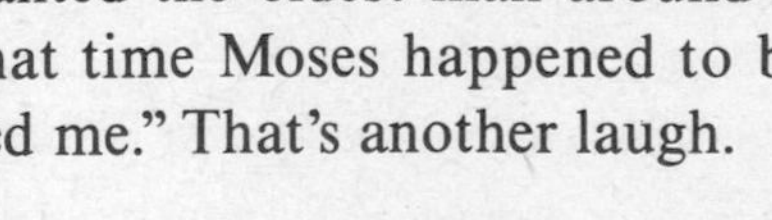

Age jokes never miss. Well, almost never. Recently I played a college, and after the show some of the kids came back to see me. They asked me different questions, and one kid wanted to know if I really started out as a dancer.

I told him I had. Then I thought I would throw in a little age joke. I said, "One time I asked Betsy Ross to go out dancing, but she couldn't—she was busy sewing something."

The kids just stared at me. Now to most people that would be funny because it means I was around when Betsy Ross was, and also that I was too dumb to know she was sewing the flag. Well, one of the kids stopped staring and asked me if Betsy Ross was a good dancer. Another wanted to know why Betsy Ross couldn't have stopped sewing, danced with me, and then started sewing again. A third thought Betsy Ross was Diana Ross's sister, and the fourth said, "Who's Diana Ross?"

That's when I said, "Kids, the interview is over." I don't mind laying an egg on the stage, but not in my dressing room.

How do you live to be 100 or more? There are certain things you have to do. The most important one is you have to be sure to make it to 99.

People keep asking me, "George, you're 87, how do you do it? You make pictures, you do television, you give concerts, you record albums, smoke cigars, drink martinis, you go out with pretty girls—how do you do it?"

It's very simple. One thing I do is exercises. Also, I walk a lot. Most people agree that walking is good for your health. And yet where I live in Beverly Hills nobody walks. If they have to go three blocks, they drive. Some people even have two, three, or four cars. I've got one neighbor who has a little car to drive to his big car.

Now me, every morning I get up and go out in my backyard, and rain or shine I walk for a mile and a half. I've got a regular routine. I walk through the yard, around the pool, through the trees and back to where I started. And I do this forty times. That covers the mile and a half.

My advice is to walk whenever you can. It's free, costs nothing, and it not only makes you live longer and feel better, but it also keeps you looking trim. But, like anything else, you can overdo walking, too. A friend of mine from Beverly Hills has been walking five miles a day for six months. He called me last week and told me he was just passing through Vancouver and would I like him to send me some canned salmon.

If you want to live to be 100 or older, you can't just sit around waiting for it to happen. You have to get up each day and go after it. We're talking here about perhaps the most important key to longevity. Besides walking, I have a whole program of exercises that I do every day. There are many different exercise programs with many different objectives. Mine is to keep me limber, toned up, and feeling good. Look, I'm not trying to get any taller or build up a lot of big muscles I can't use. Anyway, my exercise program takes about a half hour, and I do it every morning before breakfast.

If you ask me what is the single most important key to longevity, I would have to say it is avoiding worry, stress, and tension. And if you didn't ask me, I'd still have to say it.

I know I just said that exercise is the most important key to longevity, but that was when I was writing about exercise. That's the way I write.

Now, let's see if I know what I'm talking about. What is the difference between worry, stress, and tension? I really don't know. They're not exactly the same. They overlap and run into each other. Worry leads to stress, and stress leads to tension.

Okay, what are some of the things people worry about these days? Well—they're afraid the world will be blown up, crime on the streets and in their homes, overpopulation, gray hair, wrinkles, traffic congestion, parking tickets, marriage, divorce, houseguests, medical bills, inflation, flying saucers, too much salt, too much sugar, too much chlorine in the water, not enough chlorine in the water...I could go on and on, and I think I will...there's depression, unemployment, sharks...that's enough.

It's not that there haven't always been things to worry about, but when there were just newspapers we weren't aware of them as much. Radio and television have brought them right into our homes. At four o'clock in the afternoon the news starts, and from then until 7:30 all you see are explosions, wars, fires, murders, crashes...You very seldom see a cute little Girl Scout selling cookies. I love cookies; I hate sharks. And in case you start feeling good again, along comes the 11 o'clock news with a rerun of the whole thing, so you'll be sure to get a good night's sleep.

I don't know about you, but the way I figure, I can't change the world, but I can change the channel. Which is exactly what I did last night.

What do you think I got? Bela Lugosi biting three beautiful girls on their necks. It scared the hell out of me. I switched back to the news, watched a half hour of it, and slept like a baby.

Let's get serious for a moment. Worry, stress, and tension are not only unpleasant, but they can shorten your life. When your body is under stress, it manufactures certain chemicals that poison your whole system, lower your resistance, and raise your blood pressure. And we all know that high blood pressure is the major cause of strokes and heart attacks.

My attitude is, if something is beyond your control—if you can't do anything about it—there's no point worrying about it. And if you can do something about it, then there's still nothing to worry about. I feel that way when the plane I'm on is bouncing around in turbulence. It's not my problem. The pilot gets a lot of money to fly that plane; let him worry about it. True, I never fly in those small, private planes, but that's for a different reason. If I'm going down, I want to have an audience with me.

I can honestly say I was not even uptight about my heart bypass several years ago. I don't mean to minimize that operation—I would have preferred to have had my fingernails cut—but once again, what could I do about it? It was beyond my control. Besides, the surgeon had trained for years in medical school, he'd done this operation many times...and he had long, strong fingers. I had such confidence in him that I didn't give it a second thought.

When I came out of the anesthetic, I heard the surgeon say, "George, you did great, you're just fine."

I said, "Doctor, I wasn't the least bit concerned."

"Really?" he said. "I was a nervous wreck."

Even that didn't bother me. Then he handed me his bill, and I passed out.

If you want to live to be over 100, you've got to have a positive attitude. Even if you're going to fail, be positive about it. That way you'll be a successful failure.

Another attitude I'm in favor of is thinking young. As they get older, too many people tend to hang around with each other and compare ailments and gravy stains. That might be fun, but it's good to mix with younger people, too. Some older people get depressed around young people. It reminds them of how young they used to be themselves. Not me. I look at those young people and see how young I still am.

Look, I don't want anyone to get the idea that I don't like old people. I love old people. Some of my best friends were old. Let me clear something up for you. When I say I *think* young, it doesn't mean I'm trying to *be* young.

When I talk about thinking young, I'm talking about enthusiasm, keeping active, having plans, projects for tomorrow, meeting people, doing things; I look to the future because that's where I'm going to spend the rest of my life. A lot of people are too quick to decide that their life is over. And if you really think your life is over, and you have no place to go, I advise you to take very short steps. It'll take you longer to get there.

I feel sorry for people who live in the past. I know it was cheaper then, and I know that some people had very interesting pasts, but you can't keep looking in a rearview mirror—unless you enjoy having a stiff neck. Old memories are fine, but you've still got time to make new memories.

I don't live in the past. I live in a house in Beverly Hills. It's more comfortable. Actually, you may not believe this, but it's true. I don't surround myself with memorabilia. I don't waste time looking through scrapbooks of my career or rereading my old reviews—they were painful enough to read the first time. I don't even watch my old movies. I'm not interested in what happened yesterday. I find it's best to fall in love with what you're doing today. The things I did yesterday I was in love with yesterday. But that romance is over.

There's an old saying, "Life begins at 40." That's silly—life begins every morning when you wake up. Old sayings...why are the sayings always old? Like "Life is just a bowl of cherries"—why aren't there new sayings? I think I'll make up a new saying: "Life is just a bowl of tangerines."

Okay, back to attitude. Just because you're old it doesn't mean you can't lead a full, vigorous, and active life. Open your mind to it, don't just sit there—do things. Swim the English Channel; find a cure for the common cold; be the first to go over Niagara Falls in a rocking chair; think of some new old sayings. You see, the possibilities are endless.

If all else fails, try doing something nice for somebody who doesn't expect it. You'll be surprised how good you feel. The Boy Scouts have the right idea. Many's the time I've helped a young lady across the street. You should see all my merit badges.

The point is, with a good positive attitude and a little bit of luck, there's no reason you can't live to be 100. Once you've done that you've really got it made, because very few people die over 100.

---

1 **Understanding the Reading.** Answer the following questions in good sentence form.

1. In this reading selection, George Burns mixes humor in with his advice about how to live to be 100. What is funny about each of the following stories?

   His Moses story: ______________________________

   The story about his friend in Vancouver: ______________________________

   The story about his bypass surgery: ______________________________

2. Describe how George Burns "laid an egg" while talking to the college students in his dressing room.

3. According to Mr. Burns, when does life begin? Do you think this is a good attitude to have?

4. What does Mr. Burns mean by "thinking young"? How do people who "think young" act?

2 **More Old and Not-So-Old Sayings.** Put the letter of the best answer on the line to the left.

_____ 1. Which sentence from the reading indicates that George Burns might agree with the saying: "Never go gloomily, man with a mind! Hope is a better companion than fear."

(a) "George, I'd like to die today."
(b) "Even if you're going to fail, be positive about it."
(c) "Then he handed me his bill, and I passed out."
(d) "Worry leads to stress, and stress leads to tension."

_____ 2. Which saying supports George Burns's advice about worrying?

(a) "No one has ever complained about his parachute not opening."
(b) "It's not what you don't know that hurts you; it's what you suspect."
(c) "Your conscience is that still small voice that makes you feel still smaller."
(d) "One reason why we all grow wise so slowly is because we nurse our mistakes so fondly."

_____ 3. The saying, "Reputation is a large bubble that bursts when you try to blow it up yourself," is similar in meaning to _____.

(a) "Pride goes before the fall."
(b) "Sometimes a proud bearing is only the result of a stiff neck."
(c) "The trouble with being a good sport is that you have to lose to prove it."
(d) "Opportunity must knock, but all temptation has to do is stand outside and whistle."

_____ 4. "He who takes but never gives may last for years but never lives" is good advice for _____.

(a) Johnny Appleseed (b) Pinocchio (c) Prince Charming (d) Scrooge

_____ 5. Who would be *least* likely to pay attention to the advice offered in this saying: "When a person points a finger at someone else, he should remember that four fingers are pointing at himself"?

(a) an accuser (b) a conformist (c) an inspector (d) a protector

_____ 6. The person who lives by the saying, "A good boss is someone who takes a little more than his share of the blame and a little less than his share of the credit," demonstrates _____.

(a) oppression (b) squeamishness (c) strife (d) wisdom

_____ 7. The saying, "If yo think yo don't amont to mch, look what happens when we leave yo ot," might cheer up a person suffering from a bad case of _____.

(a) self-contempt (b) self-control (c) self-discipline (d) self-interest

3 Vocabulary Review.

Part A: From the choices listed, choose the word that is the best example of the word in bold-faced type and write it on the line to the right.

1. **memorabilia:**	fantasies	fossils	luxuries	trophies	________
2. **anniversary:**	bar mitzvah	birthday	ceremony	invitation	________
3. **goddess:**	Frigga	Odin	Tyr	Woden	________
4. **Scandinavian:**	Austrian	Dutch	Swedish	Swiss	________
5. **organism:**	fossil	primrose	regulator	specimen	________
6. **anesthetic:**	aspirin	ether	nicotine	penicillin	________
7. **fiction:**	memoirs	novel	publicity	testimony	________
8. **official:**	activist	candidate	mayor	psychologist	________

Part B: From the choices listed, choose the word that best describes the word in bold-faced type and write it on the line to the right.

1. **tangerine:**	essential	massive	perishable	vital	________
2. **maze:**	disorganized	infinite	intricate	reinforced	________
3. **immigrant:**	confident	recognizable	uprooted	vigorous	________
4. **scholar:**	cynical	indisputable	learned	liberal	________
5. **marvel:**	infinite	treacherous	vital	wondrous	________
6. **millisecond:**	boundless	finite	incomparable	indefinite	________
7. **braggart:**	philosophic	pretentious	sociable	unbiased	________
8. **imagery:**	excessive	expressive	instinctive	objective	________

4 **More Common Prefixes.** Use a dictionary to help you match the words listed at the left with the correct definitions. The first one has been done to get you started.

1. **ab**—*away, from, off*

abduct
abnormal
absentee
abstain
abstract

abnormal a. departing from the rule or norm
_____ b. not in residence
_____ c. to kidnap; to carry off
_____ d. to do without something by choice
_____ e. not easily understood; not dealing with anything specific; general

2. **anti**—*against*

antibiotic
antiseptic
antidote
antimacassar
antisocial

_____ a. thoroughly clean
_____ b. shunning the society of others
_____ c. a remedy to counteract the effects of a poison
_____ d. a protective covering for the backs of chairs and sofas
_____ e. any substance such as penicillin used in the prevention and treatment of disease

3. **fore**—*before, in front of*

forebear
forebode
foremost
foresight
foretell

_____ a. ahead of all others, especially in rank
_____ b. an ancestor
_____ c. the act of looking forward
_____ d. to prophesy; to predict
_____ e. to be a warning of; to sense beforehand, as a coming evil

4. **post**—*after*

posterior
posterity
postmortem
postpone
postscript

_____ a. a message added at the end of a letter
_____ b. future generations
_____ c. located behind or toward the back part
_____ d. occurring or done after death
_____ e. to delay until a future time

5. **trans**—*across, beyond*, or *above*

transcribe
transfix
transform
transgress
transplant

______________ a. to change significantly the form or appearance of

______________ b. to go beyond a limit or boundary; to trespass or sin

______________ c. to pierce through; to make motionless, as with fear or awe

______________ d. to transfer from one place or residence to another

______________ e. to copy or recopy from an original; to make a written copy of

5 **Can You Crack the Code?** The outline below is of one of the fifty states. The star represents the city that almost completely surrounds Beverly Hills, where George Burns lives. Can you crack the code to discover the name of this state and city and an interesting piece of information about the city? The L's have been filled in to get you started.

```
L          L       L
C H V  P Y N J C J V,  D P C R X H E Y R P
  (city)                   (state)
```

```
                 L              L            L       L
K B J  X H W E  V T F I H C V  H Y  K B J  C H V  P Y N J C J V  V J P C

E J A E J V J Y K  K B J  X H W E  N H G J E Y F J Y K V  R Y

K B R V  D R K T ' V  B R V K H E T:  V A P R Y,  F J M R D H,  K B J

    L                    L
D P C R X H E Y R P  E J A W I C R D,  P Y Z  K B J  W Y R K J Z

V K P K J V.
```

Lesson 9

What Will the Future Bring?

Words for Study

dimension	astrologer	resuscitate	cosmic
Pharaohs	Julius Caesar	seers	aliens
oracles	soothsayer	heritage	inevitable
Delphi	extensive	interpretation	ere

What Will the Future Bring?

The oracle at Delphi

What will the future bring? This question about that unknown dimension of time has aroused people's curiosity throughout the ages. This reading explores some of the ways in which people have attempted to learn of the events which the future holds in store for them.

* * *

For some six thousand years mankind has concerned itself with prophesying the future by way of astrology. Astrology is the study of heavenly bodies with the intent of predicting their influence on the course of human affairs. The ancient Egyptians were among the earliest, so far as it is known, to develop and use the art of prophecy. Believed without question by Pharaohs and the common people alike, prophecy was an everyday occurrence, nearly always performed by the priests. It was part of their regular priestly training to learn the methods of foretelling the future and to practice these methods upon request. In particular, they were required to predict the fortunes of the Pharaohs and of the nation of Egypt.

From Egypt astrology spread to Greece, where famous oracles were found at Delphi and other sites. There, temples were presided over by priestesses, through whom the gods would speak their prophecies. Often, the prophecies were so vague or puzzling that the results were disastrous. When Cyrus the Great, King of Persia, attacked Greece in 546 B.C., King Croesus tried to stop him and expected to succeed because the oracle at Delphi had told him he would "destroy a great empire." Croesus assumed that the empire meant was Persia, but instead he destroyed his own. Afterwards Croesus is said to have commented sadly, "No one is so foolish as to prefer war to peace, in which, instead of sons burying their fathers, fathers bury their sons. But the gods willed it so."

The Jews, too, relied on prophecy, and their generations of famous prophets are known to us through the Bible—Isaiah, Jeremiah, Ezekiel, and Daniel, as well as the twelve minor prophets.

Ancient China developed its own system of astrology. Prophecy by this and other means was considered very important in China from about 2700 B.C.—especially at the court, where there was an official astrologer. From the ninth century B.C. right up until the present, the *I Ching* or *Book of Changes* has been used by rich and poor alike to foretell their personal futures.

The Romans possessed a complex system of oracles and professional seers to foretell future events. Although many stories are recorded of their fulfillment, these prophecies were not always believed. As we know from William Shakespeare's play, *Julius Caesar*, the Roman statesman and dictator Julius Caesar disregarded a seer's warning about the Ides of March (March 15th):

Soothsayer:	Beware the Ides of March.
Caesar:	What man is that?
Brutus:	A soothsayer bids you beware the Ides of March.
Caesar:	Set him before me; let me see his face.
Cassius:	Fellow, come from the throng; look upon Caesar.
Caesar:	What say'st thou to me now? Speak once again.
Soothsayer:	Beware the Ides of March.
Caesar:	He is a dreamer. Let us leave him.

On the Ides of March, 44 B.C., Caesar was stabbed to death in the Senate by Cassius, Brutus, and others.

At one time or another the Romans also made use of an extensive range of other methods of prophecy, including dreams, fire, water, entrails, mirrors, and the fall of dice.

In Britain the Celts, one of the ancient peoples of western Europe, established an early tradition of prophecy. Sacrifices were made—of bulls in times of peace and of men in times of war. These men, most frequently prisoners, are said to have been inserted into hollow, man-shaped figures of wickerwork, which were then burned. From the sounds of their cries and of the flames, the prophecy was made.

Much later, in the fifth century A.D., there was the puzzling figure of Merlin, a famous magician and prophet who has since become an important part of British mythology. According to Geoffrey of Monmouth, a 12th century English writer, Merlin made a series of puzzling predictions covering events of the next ten thousand years and more.

Probably the greatest of all the astrological prophets, in that his precise prophecies have been proven surprisingly accurate for a number of centuries after his death, was Nostradamus. He was a Frenchman, Michel de Notredame, who lived from 1503 to 1566. A practicing physician, Nostradamus found time to make prophecies of events ranging in time from his immediate future up to the year A.D. 7000.

All his long-range predictions are presented in puzzling verses in which many of the proper names are given in the form of clues and the facts are deliberately hidden. With hindsight, it is possible to untangle the apparent meaning of most verses. Thus, among Nostradamus's writings are predictions of London's great plague and fire, the French Revolution, Napoleon, the Russian Revolution and World War II (in which he refers to "Hister," which seems to be astonishingly close to Hitler).

The prophecies of Nostradamus which relate to our own future are impossible to interpret with any degree of certainty:

In the year 1999 in the Seventh month,
A great king of frightfulness will come
from the skies
To resuscitate the great king of Angumois,
Around this time Mars will reign for the
good cause.

Although Angumois certainly refers to France, the remainder of the verse is not clear. Could the "great king of frightfulness...from the skies" refer to missiles launched from satellites, or is it a warning of an invasion from outer space? Can Mars be taken as standing for war, or is it a reference to the planet?

There have been many other well-known seers who form a clear heritage to present-day prophets and to the daily "What Your Stars Foretell" columns, which appear in most newspapers. It must be remembered that almost all prophecies of this kind are short-term and personal. They rarely attempt to describe the future of society. Yet these more recent predictions are evidence of an early and continuous awareness of the existence of a future and of the fact that the future will be different from the present.

Another popular form of foretelling the future is the interpretation of dreams. It has been believed for thousands of years that dreams reflect the past and future—even that while one is dreaming, one's mind is actually visiting portions of one's past or future existence and experiencing them. This idea was revived in a book published in 1927 entitled *An Experiment with Time* in which the author, J.W. Dunne, proved to his own satisfaction that a careful recording and analysis of dreams will produce detailed prophecies of one's own future or occasionally, generally indirectly, of the futures of other people.

People's interest in the future is not confined to traditional forms of prophecy. One of the popular forms of prophecy in the 20th century is predictive fiction. The majority of predictive stories offer strong warnings of some kind about the future. In 1914, for example, *The World Set Free* was published. The author of this novel was the famous British writer H.G. Wells. In the novel, Wells cautioned against the development of new weapons of war. In particular, he included a description of "atomic bombs," which were dropped by hand from open aircraft and went on exploding forever. *The World Set Free* was not the first novel to use the term "atomic bomb"; it had been used in a novel written in 1895.

Since 1945, the year in which the United States dropped the first atomic bombs on Japan, predicting the future has become a growth industry. Science fiction—of which tales about the future make up the major part—has tended to increase its sales almost every year. The theme of most of these novels has been gloomy, showing a wasted earth without much hope for the survival of mankind. The disasters come in a variety of forms: too much heat, too little heat, too much water, too little water, plague, war, cosmic disasters, and many more.

A large proportion of post-1945 tales of the future have featured contact with aliens. In more recent science fiction, humans and aliens need no longer fight at first sight, however distasteful they find each other's personal appearance. Alien races are no longer considered more or less intelligent, or more or less advanced than we are; they are just different.

The German poet Johann Schiller once wrote:

Yet, I would not call them
Voices of warning, that announce to us
Only the inevitable. As the sun,
Ere it is risen, sometimes points its image
In the atmosphere—so often do the spirits
Of great events stride on before the events,
And in today already walks tomorrow.

—from Coleridge's translation of
Schiller's *Wallenstein*

Predicting the future of prophecies and tales of the future is a risky business. It seems certain, however, that in light of mankind's desire to know what tomorrow will bring, tales of prediction will always be with us—so long as there is a future.

From *The Shapes of Futures Past* by Chris Morgan.

1 **Understanding the Reading.** In good sentence form, briefly explain how Mr. Morgan relates each of the following to his theme of mankind's interest in the future.

1. The Egyptians: ____________________
____
2. King Croesus: ____________________
____
3. Jeremiah: ____________________
____
4. *I Ching*: ____________________
____
5. Julius Caesar: ____________________
____
6. The Celts: ____________________
____
7. Merlin: ____________________
____
8. Nostradamus: ____________________
____
9. Post-World War II science fiction: ____________________
____
10. Johann Schiller: ____________________
____

2 **What Do You Think?** If you were to go to a fortuneteller, what would you hope he or she would tell you about the following aspects of your future? Write your answers in good sentence form.

1. Occupation: ______________________________
____
2. Place of residence: ______________________________
____
3. Romance/marriage: ______________________________
____
4. Family life: ______________________________
____
5. Friends: ______________________________
____
6. Money: ______________________________
____
7. Travel/adventure: ______________________________
____

3

Word Relationships. Write the letter of the answer that best completes each statement on the line to the left.

_____ 1. Steady is to inconsistent as _____.

(a) alien is to Mars
(b) cosmic is to exceptional
(c) efficient is to wasteful
(d) essential is to unreliable

_____ 2. Julius Caesar is to Roman as _____.

(a) Croesus is to Persian
(b) Cyrus is to Greek
(c) Isaiah is to Egyptian
(d) Nostradamus is to French

_____ 3. ! is to exclamation point as _____.

(a) * is to asterisk
(b) ' is to contraction
(c) ? is to question
(d) " is to quotation

_____ 4. Broad is to extensive as _____.

(a) astrological is to idealistic
(b) finite is to limited
(c) Mesozoic is to fossilized
(d) priestly is to saintly

_____ 5. Ezekiel is to prophet as _____.

(a) H.G. Wells is to astrology
(b) Pharoah is to Greece
(c) Shakespeare is to playwright
(d) Delphi is to oracle

_____ 6. Lizard is to reptile as _____.

(a) mariner is to sea
(b) loner is to antisocial
(c) penicillin is to antibiotic
(d) sofa is to antimacassar

_____ 7. Forebear is to ancestor as _____.

(a) priest is to priestess
(b) seer is to soothsayer
(c) magician is to nonconformist
(d) statesman is to dictator

_____ 8. Siesta is to nap as _____.

(a) tornado is to breeze
(b) fiesta is to celebration
(c) peso is to cost
(d) burro is to mule

_____ 9. Thorn is to prickly as _____.

(a) error is to glaring
(b) interpretation is to abstract
(c) likelihood is to inevitable
(d) misconception is to faulty

_____ 10. Gobi is to desert as _____.

(a) appendix is to operation
(b) brontosaurus is to phylum
(c) postscript is to letter
(d) Titanic is to ocean liner

4 **Still More Prefixes.** From the list at the left, choose the word which best completes each sentence and write it in the blank.

1. **con**—*with*, *together*, *jointly*

concocted concurred conferred conformed	Hiram Emory and his companion Norah Pace were walking to a nearby coffee shop after attending a lecture. Although both ________________ that the lecture had been a waste of time, their reasons for thinking so were quite different.

2. **pro**—*forward*, *before*

professed propelled protested provoked	"What ________________ me the most was how she kept harping on how important it is to live in the here and now," complained Norah Pace.

3. **ad**—*near to*, *to*

adhere adjoin administer adopt	"You're absolutely right," exclaimed Hiram. "How can anyone ________________ to such a foolish notion when reflecting on 'the good old days' is what helps to make life bearable."

4. **contra**—*against*, *opposing*, or *contrary*

contradiction contradictory contrary contrast	"On the ________________," replied the shocked Ms. Pace, "people should put the past behind them. Everyone knows that planning ahead is absolutely essential!"

5. **e**—*out*, *out of*, *from*

ejected elapsed eluded emitted	Hiram ________________ a disapproving growl in spite of himself. "Are you suggesting that we spend all our time thinking about the future?"

6. **per**—*through*, *throughout*

permissible permissive permanent perpetual	"Well, of course it's ________________ to dwell on past events," retorted Norah rather rudely, "if you have no ambition to *be* somebody!"

7. **super**—*above, on, over*

supercharged
superduper
superficial
supernatural

"And I suppose, with all your plans for a ________________ future, you consider yourself a superior human being?" Hiram shot back in an equally rude voice.

8. **semi**—*half*

semicircle
semifinal
semiformal
semiprecious

"Have you ever considered that you've never made it to the ________________ round at the club's tennis tournament because you're too busy thinking about what a great athlete you were in high school?" Norah suggested smugly.

9. **sub**—*under*

subdivide
submerge
submit
subsist

"Don't expect me to ________________ to such insults!" shouted Hiram angrily. "The reason you've never once been promoted at the office is that you're forever dreaming of next week, next month, next year!"

10. **circum**—*around*

circumference
circumstance
circumstantial
circumvent

This dispute was never resolved for so absorbed were they in their argument that they failed to ________________ a mammoth pothole that lay directly in their path. Hiram sprained his ankle, and their attention turned to getting him home where he could soak it.

5 **A Look Back.** William Shakespeare was mentioned in this reading selection. Shakespeare (1564-1616), who wrote *Julius Caesar*, is best known for his plays, but he also wrote poems and songs. The song below appears in *Love's Labor Lost*, another of his plays. Read the song and then answer the questions which follow.

Winter

When icicles hang by the wall,
And Dick the shepherd blows his nail,
And Tom bears logs into the hall,
And milk comes frozen home in pail,
When blood is nipped, and ways be foul,
Then nightly sings the staring owl,
To-whit!
To-who!—a merry note,
While greasy Joan doth keel* the pot. *stir

When all aloud the wind doth blow,
And coughing drowns the parson's saw,* *wise saying
And birds brooding in the snow,
And Marian's nose looks red and raw,
When roasted crabs* hiss in the bowl, *crab apples
Then nightly sings the staring owl,
To-whit!
To-who!—a merry note,
While greasy Joan doth keel the pot.

1. Do you think the setting for this song is the country or the city? Cite evidence from the song to support your answer.

____

____

2. List two images, or pictures, of winter that William Shakespeare might still have used if he had written this song during your lifetime.

a. ______________________________

b. ______________________________

3. List two images of winter that Shakespeare would probably not have used if he had written this song during your lifetime.

a. ______________________________

b. ______________________________

4. List two images you would use if you were to write a song describing winter as you experience it.

a. ______________________________

b. ______________________________

Lesson 10

All Summer in a Day

Words for Study

muffled	repercussions	savored	sever
avalanche	tremor	solemn	Cairo
volcanic	resilient	innovation	coroner
apparatus	suspend	negotiate	desecration

All Summer in a Day

by Ray Bradbury

"Ready?"

"Ready."

"Now?"

"Soon."

"Do the scientists really know? Will it happen today, will it?"

"Look, look; see for yourself!"

The children pressed to each other like so many roses, so many weeds, intermixed, peering out for a look at the hidden sun.

It rained.

It had been raining for seven years; thousands upon thousands of days compounded and filled from one end to the other with rain, with the drum and gush of water, with the sweet crystal fall of showers and the concussion of storms so heavy they were tidal waves come over the islands. A thousand forests had been crushed under the rain and grown up a thousand times to be crushed again. And this was the way life was forever on the planet Venus, and this was the schoolroom of the children of the rocket men and women who had come to a raining world to set up civilization and live out their lives.

"It's stopping, it's stopping!"

"Yes, yes!"

Margot stood apart from them, from these children who could never remember a time when there wasn't rain and rain and rain. They were all nine years old, and if there had been a day, seven years ago, when the sun came out for an hour and showed its face to the stunned world, they could not recall. Sometimes, at night, she heard them stir in remembrance and she knew they were dreaming and remembering gold or a yellow crayon or a coin large enough to buy the world with. She knew they thought they remembered a warmness, like a blushing in the face, in the body, in the arms and legs and trembling hands. But then they always awoke to the tatting drum, the endless shaking down of clear bead necklaces upon the roof, the walk, the gardens, the forests, and their dreams were gone.

All day yesterday they had read in class about the sun. About how like a lemon it was, and how hot. And they had written small stories or essays or poems about it:

I think the sun is a flower,
That blooms for just one hour.

That was Margot's poem, read in a quiet voice in the still classroom while the rain was falling outside.

"Aw, you didn't write that!" protested one of the boys.

"I did," said Margot. "I *did.*"

"William!" said the teacher.

But that was yesterday. Now the rain was slackening, and the children were crushed in the great thick windows.

"Where's teacher?"

"She'll be back."

"She'd better hurry, we'll miss it!"

They turned on themselves, like a feverish wheel, all tumbling spokes.

Margot stood alone. She was a very frail girl who looked as if she had been lost in the rain for years and the rain had washed out the blue from her eyes and the red from her mouth and the yellow from her hair. She was an old photograph dusted from an album, whitened away, and if she spoke at all her voice would be a ghost. Now she stood, separate, staring at the rain and the loud wet world beyond the huge glass.

"What're *you* looking at?" said William.

Margot said nothing.

"Speak when you're spoken to." He gave her a shove. But she did not move; rather she let herself be moved only by him and nothing else.

They edged away from her, they would not look at her. She felt them go away. And this was because she would play no games with them in the echoing tunnels of the underground city. If they tagged her and ran, she stood blinking after them and did not follow. When the class sang songs about happiness and life and games her lips barely moved. Only when they sang about the sun and the summer did her lips move as she watched the drenched windows.

And then, of course, the biggest crime of all was that she had come here only five years ago from Earth, and she remembered the sun and the way the sun was and the sky was when she was four in Ohio. And they, they had been on Venus all their lives, and they had been only two years old when last the sun came out and had long since forgotten the color and heat of it and the way it really was. But Margot remembered.

"It's like a penny," she said once, eyes closed.

"No it's not!" the children cried.

"It's like a fire," she said, "in the stove."

"You're lying, you don't remember!" cried the children.

But she remembered and stood quietly apart from all of them and watched the patterning windows. And once, a month ago, she had refused to shower in the school shower rooms, had clutched her hands to her ears and over her head, screaming the water mustn't touch her head. So after that, dimly, dimly, she sensed it, she was different and they knew her difference and kept away.

There was talk that her father and mother were taking her back to Earth next year; it seemed vital to her that they do so, though it would mean the loss of thousands of dollars to her family. And so, the children hated her for all these reasons of big and little consequence. They hated her pale snow face, her waiting silence, her thinness, and her possible future.

"Get away!" The boy gave her another push. "What're you waiting for?"

Then, for the first time, she turned and looked at him. And what she was waiting for was in her eyes.

"Well, don't wait around here!" cried the boy savagely. "You won't see nothing!"

Her lips moved.

"Nothing!" he cried. "It was all a joke, wasn't it?" He turned to the other children. "Nothing's happening today. *Is* it?"

They all blinked at him and then, understanding, laughed and shook their heads. "Nothing, nothing!"

"Oh, but," Margot whispered, her eyes helpless. "But this is the day, the scientists predict, they say, they *know*, the sun...."

"All a joke!" said the boy, and seized her roughly. "Hey, everyone, let's put her in a closet before teacher comes!"

"No," said Margot, falling back.

They surged about her, caught her up and bore her, protesting, and then pleading, and then crying, back into a tunnel, a room, a closet, where they slammed and locked the door. They stood looking at the door and saw it tremble from her beating and throwing herself against it. They heard her muffled cries. Then, smiling, they turned and went out and back down the tunnel, just as the teacher arrived.

"Ready, children?" She glanced at her watch.

"Yes!" said everyone.

"Are we all here?"

"Yes!"

The rain slackened still more.

They crowded to the huge door.

The rain stopped.

It was as if, in the midst of a film, concerning an avalanche, a tornado, a hurricane, a volcanic eruption, something had, first gone wrong with the sound apparatus, thus muffling and finally cutting off all noise, all of the blasts and repercussions and thunders, and then, second, ripped the film from the projector and inserted in its place a peaceful tropical slide which did not move or tremor. The world ground to a standstill. The silence was so immense and unbelievable that you felt your ears had been stuffed or you had lost your hearing altogether. The children put their hands to their ears. They stood apart. The door slid back and the smell of the silent, waiting world came in to them.

The sun came out.

It was the color of flaming bronze and it was very large. And the sky around it was a blazing blue tile color. And the jungle burned with sunlight as the children, released from their spell, rushed out, yelling into the springtime.

"Now, don't go too far," called the teacher after them. "You've only two hours, you know. You wouldn't want to get caught out!"

But they were running and turning their faces up to the sky and feeling the sun on their cheeks like a warm iron; they were taking off their jackets and letting the sun burn their arms.

"Oh, it's better than the sun lamps, isn't it?"

"Much, much better!"

They stopped running and stood in the great jungle that covered Venus, that grew and never stopped growing, tumultuously, even as you watched it. It was a nest of octopi, clustering up great arms of fleshlike weed, wavering, flowering this brief spring. It was the color of rubber and ash, this jungle, from the many years without sun. It was the color of stones and white cheeses and ink, and it was the color of the moon.

The children lay out, laughing, on the jungle mattress, and heard it sigh and squeak under them, resilient and alive. They ran among the trees, they slipped and fell, they pushed each other, they played hide-and-seek and tag, but most of all they squinted at the sun until the tears ran down their faces, they put their hands up to the yellowness and that amazing blueness and they breathed of the fresh, fresh air and listened and listened to the silence which suspended them in a blessed sea of no sound and no motion. They looked at everything and savored everything. Then, wildly, like animals escaped from their caves, they ran and ran in shouting circles. They ran for an hour and did not stop running.

And then—

In the midst of their running one of the girls wailed.

Everyone stopped.

The girl, standing in the open, held out her hand.

"Oh, look, look," she said, trembling.

They came slowly to look at her opened palm.

In the center of it, cupped and huge, was a single raindrop.

She began to cry, looking at it.

They glanced quietly at the sky.

"Oh. Oh."

A few cold drops fell on their noses and their cheeks and their mouths. The sun faded behind a stir of mist. A wind blew cool around them. They turned and started to walk back toward the underground house, their hands at their sides, their smiles vanishing away.

A boom of thunder startled them and like leaves before a new hurricane, they tumbled upon each other and ran. Lightning struck ten miles away, five miles away, a mile, a half mile. The sky darkened into midnight in a flash.

They stood in the doorway of the underground for a moment until it was raining hard. Then they closed the door and heard the gigantic sound of the rain falling in tons and avalanches, everywhere and forever.

"Will it be seven more years?"

"Yes. Seven."

Then one of them gave a little cry.

"Margot."

They stood as if someone had driven them, like so many stakes, into the floor. They looked at each other and then looked away. They glanced out at the world that was raining now and raining and raining steadily. They could not meet each other's glances. Their faces were solemn and pale. They looked at their hands and feet, their faces down.

"Margot."

One of the girls said, "Well...?"

No one moved.

"Go on," whispered the girl.

They walked slowly down the hall in the sound of cold rain. They turned through the doorway to the room in the sound of the storm and thunder, lightning on their faces, blue and terrible. They walked over to the closet door slowly and stood by it.

Behind the closet door was only silence.

They unlocked the door, even more slowly, and let Margot out.

---

1 **Understanding the Story.** Answer the following questions in good sentence form.

1. What is the setting of "All Summer in a Day"?

2. What is special about this particular day?

3. Why do the other children dislike Margot? Be sure to include details from the story which support your answer.

4. In what way is Margot partly responsible for the tensions between her and the other children?

5. Describe what happens as a result of the conflict between Margot and the other children.

6. How much time do the children actually have to enjoy "all summer in a day"?

7. Describe the response of the children to being outside on this day.

8. How do the children seem to feel about their behavior toward Margot?

2 **What Do You Think?** Answer the following questions in good sentence form. Be sure to include reasons which help to support your opinion.

1. Do you think that the children's experience will affect their feelings about the rain?

2. In what way are the children in "All Summer in a Day" similar to children you have known?

3. What things do we now take for granted that we might no longer be able to enjoy in the future?

3 **Synonym Review.** From the choices listed, choose the best synonym for the word in bold-faced type and write it on the line to the right.

1. **ere:**	before	latter	soon	thereupon	________
2. **heritage:**	circumstance	hindsight	innovation	tradition	________
3. **cling:**	adapt	adhere	adopt	advance	________
4. **earthly:**	encrusted	moral	mortal	skeptical	________
5. **boarded:**	embalmed	embanked	embarked	embattled	________
6. **negotiate:**	bargain	bicker	reestablish	settle	________
7. **abduct:**	embezzle	kidnap	swindle	transgress	________
8. **contradict:**	contrast	dispute	profess	provoke	________
9. **convincing:**	conclusive	exclusive	inclusive	reclusive	________
10. **mammoth:**	excessive	expressive	infinite	massive	________
11. **shun:**	abstain	criticize	denounce	disapprove	________
12. **perpetual:**	aimless	ceaseless	faultless	motionless	________
13. **venture:**	ambition	calling	eruption	undertaking	________
14. **disgust:**	compel	dispel	impel	repel	________
15. **separate:**	circumvent	elude	propel	sever	________
16. **misgiving:**	contradiction	doubt	mischief	wrongdoing	________
17. **avoid:**	eject	elapse	elude	emit	________
18. **resuscitate:**	reassure	refresh	reproduce	revive	________
19. **surge:**	cluster	muffle	suspend	swell	________
20. **insight:**	conception	deception	exception	perception	________

4 **Looking Backward.** The reading in the lesson, "All Summer in a Day," takes us far into the future. Now you have a chance to look at some events that occurred in 1899—just before this century began. Use one word from each set at the left to complete these moments in history as reported in 1899 issues of the Danbury, Connecticut, *News-Times*.

composition
deposition
exposition
imposition

1. Paris: Hundreds of American horseless carriages and vehicles of all kinds will be seen on the streets of Paris during the great universal __________________ of 1900.

composed
deposed
disposed
proposed

2. Pittsburgh: Negotiations have just been made by the Westinghouse Electric and Manufacturing Company for the equipment of fourteen cars of the ordinary trolley type for use in the city of Cairo, Egypt. This line will be the first in the country but it is __________________ to build another line to the pyramids.

deceived
declined
dejected
detained

3. Fordham: Mrs. Sarah Tefft confessed to the coroner that she had shot herself during an attack of the "blues." The relatives __________________ as witnesses were discharged in court.

attained
contained
detained
obtained

4. Elmira: After marrying Nellie G. Maxwell of Williamsport, Pa., over a long distance telephone Monday night, Harry A. Rantz of this city took the first train he could get and traveled 78 miles to find his bride. Before taking this curious means of becoming man and wife, the opinions of lawyers were __________________ affirming the legality of the ceremony.

distinct
distinguished
distorted
distributed

5. Chatham: A northeast blizzard prevailed along the entire Cape Cod coast this forenoon. The sea is tremendously high and the __________________ roar of the waves could be heard on shore.

deflating
defrauding
degrading
demoting

6. Norwalk: F.T. Norton, arrested on the charge of __________________ merchants throughout the state by selling worthless soap, was brought up for trial before Judge Frost in the town court at Norwalk this morning.

ill-advised
ill-fated
ill-gotten
ill-used

7. New York: A year ago today the United States battleship *Maine* was blown up in the harbor of Havana....In many of the stores are pictures of the ________________ battleship with the phrase "Remember the *Maine*."

encountered
endangered
enrolled
envisioned

8. Manila: Keller's battalion of the Eighteenth United States Infantry ________________ a large body of enemy Filipinos occupying both sides of the road who met the advance of the American troops with a severe and well-directed fire.

affix
prefix
suffix
transfix

9. Albany: Governor Roosevelt celebrated Washington's birthday in a decision to ________________ his signature early this morning to the bill to prevent the desecration, mutilation, or improper use of the nation's flag.

reinforced
rejected
released
required

10. New Haven: Charles D. Thomas, who had hated women ever since he was jilted when a young man, died recently. He was a carpenter and lived alone with a housekeeper, whom he ________________ to leave his meals outside his door, so that he might never see her.

---

5 **The Days of Our Lives.** In 1899, a man whose name is unknown published his findings on how the average seventy-year-old American male had spent his life. Seventy years was the average life span for an American male in 1899. The bar graph below shows his findings. You may be interested to know the man calculated that three months of the average American man's life was spent just putting on and taking off his shoes! Details of this nature have not been included in the graph.

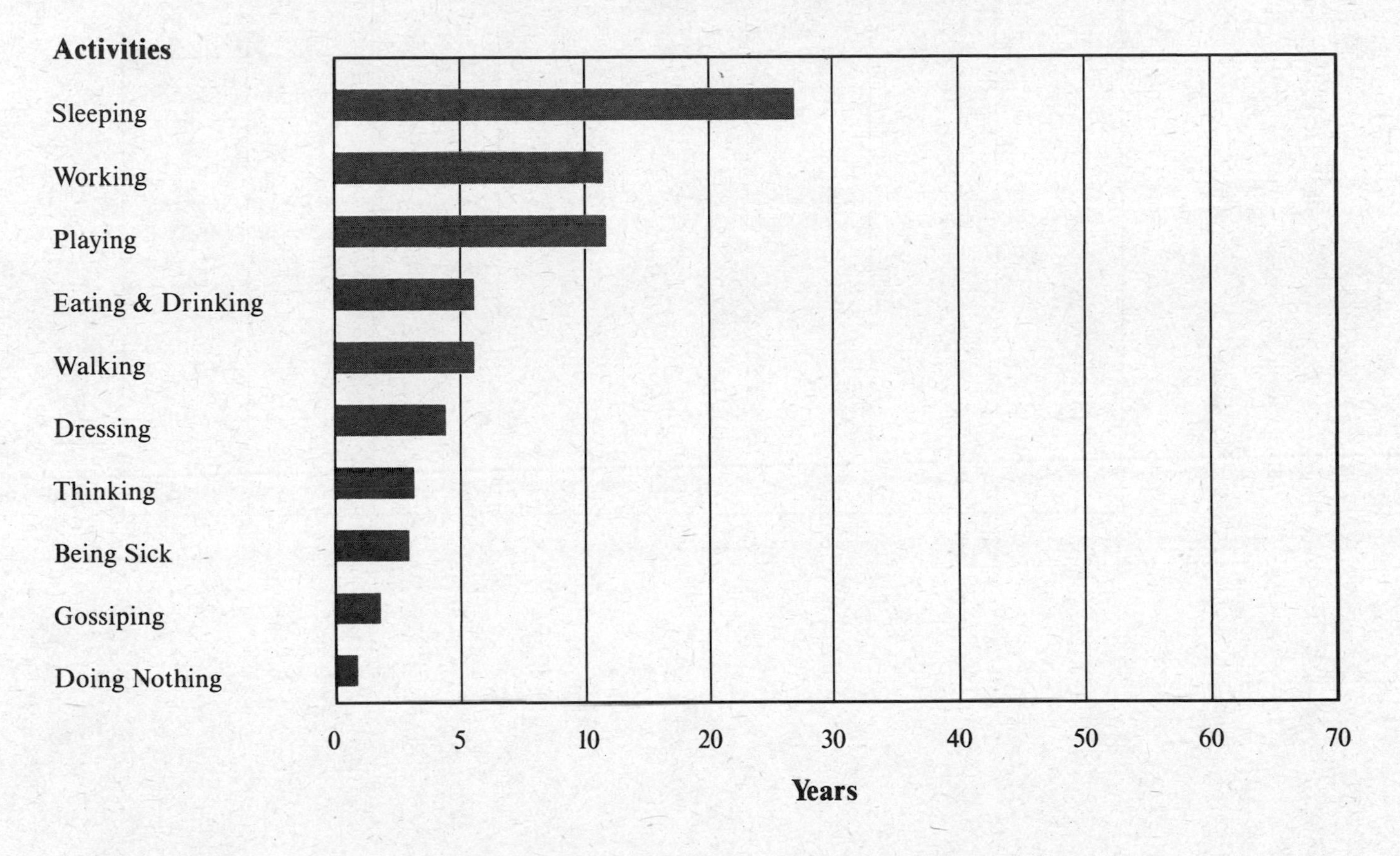

Part A. Read the statements below. If a statement is true based on the information on the graph, write **T** on the line to the left. If it is false, write **F**. Write a "**?**" if the answer cannot be determined from the information on the graph.

_____ 1. The average American male who lived during the second half of the 1800s spent more time sleeping than doing anything else.

_____ 2. The average American male who lived during the second half of the 1800s spent as much time walking as he did eating and drinking.

_____ 3. Reading is not included on the graph because back in those days men spent less time reading than putting on and taking off their shoes.

_____ 4. The average American male who lived during the second half of the 1800s spent more time working than he did playing.

_____ 5. The average American male who lived during the second half of the 1800s spent less time gossiping than did his wife.

Part B. Now design a bar graph in which you show how you spend the hours in a typical day. Include at least eight activities in your graph. Use the 1899 bar graph as a model and don't forget to title your graph.

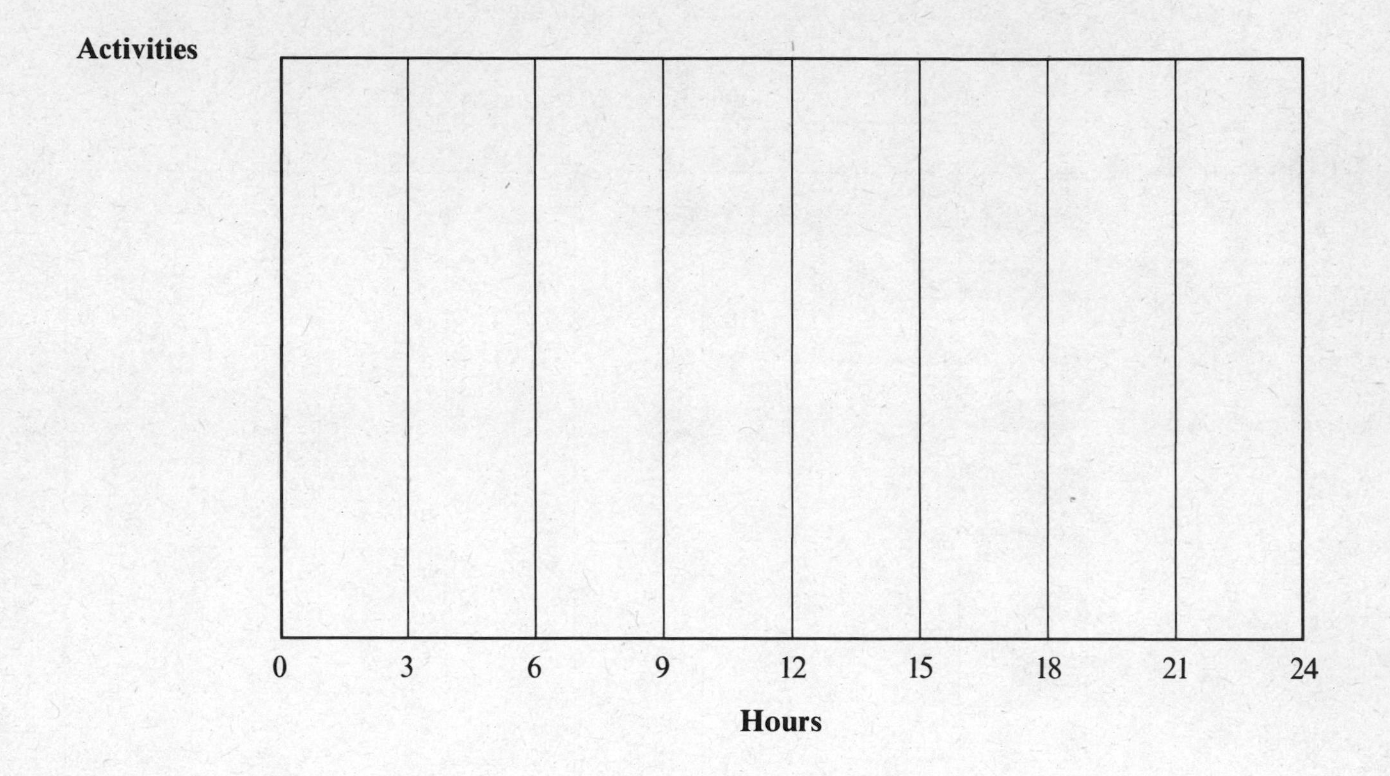

Review: Lessons 1-10

1 **Definitions.** Match the words listed below with the correct definitions.

apparatus	expedition	oracle	specimen
deposition	exposition	Pharaoh	spectacle
desecration	innovation	posterity	testimony
disruption	mariner	repercussion	tremor

________________ 1. the beginning or introduction of something new

________________ 2. a king of ancient Egypt, from an Egyptian word meaning "great house"

________________ 3. a machine or group of machines used to accomplish a specific task

________________ 4. a person considered to be a source of wise counsel or prophecy

________________ 5. a public exhibition or show, as of artistic or industrial developments

________________ 6. a public performance or display; a marvel or curiosity

________________ 7. a quick shaking movement; a nervous quiver; a thrill

________________ 8. a sailor or seaman; one who navigates a ship

________________ 9. future generations; all of a person's descendants

________________ 10. the act of abusing the holiness or sacred nature of something

________________ 11. an indirect effect, influence, or result produced by an event or action

________________ 12. an individual, item, or part that represents the whole; a sample, as of tissue, blood, or urine, used to analyze or diagnose one's health

________________ 13. any evidence in support of a fact or assertion; proof; a public declaration regarding a religious experience

________________ 14. testimony under oath; especially, a written statement by a witness for use in court in his absence

________________ 15. the act of upsetting the order of something or throwing things into confusion or disorder

________________ 16. a journey undertaken by an organized group of people with a definite objective; a long march or voyage made by military forces to the scene of a battle

2 **Vocabulary Review.** Write the letter of the best answer on the line to the left.

_____ 1. The _____ is the boundary line of a circle.
(a) arc (b) circumference (c) diameter (d) radius

_____ 2. A tourist to Egypt would probably see _____.
(a) Delphi (b) Pharaohs (c) pyramids (d) the Gobi desert

_____ 3. Who would be most anxious about the location of reefs?
(a) mariner (b) oracle (c) Pharaoh (d) scavenger

_____ 4. An _____ counteracts the effects of a poisonous substance.
(a) antibiotic (b) antidote (c) antimacassar (d) antiseptic

_____ 5. A coroner would probably be most knowledgeable about _____.
(a) assassins (b) burials (c) embalming (d) pathology

_____ 6. To which magazine would a person most likely subscribe if he wished to learn more about history?
(a) *American Heritage* (c) *National Geographic*
(b) *Country Journal* (d) *U.S. News and World Report*

_____ 7. Which of the following is an Old Testament prophet?
(a) Cassius (b) Cyrus (c) Isaiah (d) Merlin

_____ 8. A seer is noted for his _____.
(a) foresight (b) eyesight (c) hindsight (d) insight

_____ 9. _____ is the capital of Connecticut.
(a) Bridgeport (b) Hartford (c) New Haven (d) Norwalk

_____ 10. The money obtained by a swindler is _____.
(a) ill-advised (b) ill-fated (c) ill-gotten (d) ill-used

_____ 11. The term *Mesozoic* refers to a(n) _____.
(a) brontosaurus (b) era (c) geologist (d) mountain range

_____ 12. Which of the following people lives a reclusive life?
(a) gypsy (b) hermit (c) hobo (d) nomad

_____ 13. The major function of the U.S. Supreme Court is to _____ the law.
(a) administer (b) estimate (c) interpret (d) negotiate

_____ 14. *Entrails* refer mainly to an animal's _____.
(a) bloodstream (b) heart (c) intestines (d) lungs

_____ 15. The _____ were early inhabitants of Britain.
(a) Celts (b) Filipinos (c) Persians (d) Spaniards

_____ 16. Under what circumstances would a person exclaim, "Perish the thought"?
(a) He believes that misconceptions are inevitable.
(b) He is discussing something that is extinct.
(c) He is involved in a difficult negotiation.
(d) He opposes a certain idea.

3 **Antonym Review.** From the choices listed, choose the word that is the best antonym for the word in bold-faced type and write it on the line to the right.

1. **abduct:**	embezzle	release	shackle	terrorize	________
2. **disregard:**	criticize	heed	resent	transgress	________
3. **vigorous:**	inactive	inconsistent	indefinite	inefficient	________
4. **solemn:**	feverish	permissive	spirited	spiritual	________
5. **turbulence:**	anesthetic	calm	enthusiasm	relaxation	________
6. **stagnant:**	active	seasonal	sociable	varied	________
7. **limber:**	horrified	immobile	perishable	resilient	________
8. **capable:**	curious	incompetent	sociable	unreliable	________
9. **intricate:**	exclusive	minimized	purified	simple	________
10. **hasten:**	dispel	linger	negotiate	sever	________
11. **painstaking:**	abstract	careless	discredited	efficient	________
12. **repel:**	adhere	attract	prevail	provoke	________
13. **unparalleled:**	boundless	definite	ordinary	perpetual	________
14. **affirm:**	confer	deny	profess	retort	________
15. **embark:**	demote	denounce	depose	desist	________

4

More Durations. For each sentence, use *three* prefixes listed at the left to complete this information about durations correctly. The first one has been done to get you started.

con
de
pro
re
un

1. One ___re___search study has _____claimed that American teenagers _____tribute one hour of their time daily to household tasks.

con
de
e
ex
in

2. Tourists are _____formed that between one hour and one hour and ten minutes is the average length of time between _____ruptions of Old Faithful, one of the world's most _____pendable geysers.

con
de
ob
pre
re

3. Frenchmen _____vote one hour and forty-six minutes to _____suming food each day which, according to one _____server, is the highest world average for any nationality.

con
de
non
per
re

4. In one year, U.S. taxpayers are _____prived of $428 million in interest because the federal government _____tains their money, $3.9 billion, in _____-interest-paying bank accounts.

de
e
re
sub
trans

5. Fifteen days _____lapse before a physician is reasonably certain that his patient will not _____ject an organ _____plant.

con
ex
in
pro
re

6. Six days is the average length of time for county fairs, which usually _____tend from Monday through Saturday—the longest practical period for keeping animals _____fined and _____duce fresh.

---

de
ex
of
per
pro

7. Seven days is the amount of time off for good behavior ____mitted for each month of a term served for a Federal ____fense if the sentence is not less than three years and does not ____ceed five years.

com
de
re
sub
un

8. 219 days is the lifetime sleep ____quirement of a cow which, ____like a human being, ____mands only three per cent of its time for sleep.

5 **Past, Present, and Future.** The American poet Henry Wadsworth Longfellow made an interesting observation about these three dimensions of time.

- Each of the eighteen descriptions defines or gives a clue for a certain word. Write that word on the lines to the left of each description.
- Put the letters of those words in the blanks on the next page to read Longfellow's quote.
- The first one has been done for you. Study it before you begin.

T H U M B 84 77 10 33 39	1. A slang synonym for hitchhike
___ ___ ___ ___ ___ ___ 62 46 28 15 60 91	2. Leader of Germany during World War II
___ ___ ___ ___ ___ ___ ___ ___ 66 1 81 25 96 43 47 78	3. The tusks of this animal are valued for their ivory.
___ ___ ___ ___ ___ 50 93 40 57 8	4. A group of bees or other insects
___ ___ ___ ___ ___ ___ ___ 42 68 89 41 85 88 56	5. Something to put on your hamburger or french fries
___ ___ ___ ___ ___ ___ 101 13 100 79 103 83	6. "An **A** for _____"
___ ___ ___ ___ ___ ___ ___ ___ ___ 16 58 19 44 51 59 49 76 17	7. A long duration of life
___ ___ ___ 92 48 63	8. A female sheep
___ ___ ___ ___ ___ 38 72 2 20 62	9. A dentist can fix a hole in this.
___ ___ ___ ___ ___ ___ ___ ___ 21 103 71 45 36 29 67 55	10. A living thing
___ ___ ___ ___ ___ ___ ___ ___ 5 26 64 37 15 86 6 69	11. The emperor of France defeated at the Battle of Waterloo (1769-1821)
___ ___ ___ ___ ___ ___ 94 31 18 31 52 24	12. A spike of ice formed by dripping water
___ ___ ___ ___ ___ 12 98 61 70 53	13. "_____ as a fruitcake"
___ ___ ___ ___ ___ ___ 102 87 73 46 11 80	14. To declare positively

___ ___ ___ ___ ___ ___ ___
65 97 3 35 99 82 65

15. The farmer's alarm clock

___ ___ ___ ___
8 32 22 23

16. An insect that resembles a butterfly

___ ___ ___ ___ ___ ___ ___ ___ ___
9 14 95 27 4 54 11 30 27

17. The area surrounding a city

___ ___ ___ ___ ___
75 74 90 7 34

18. A highway; the territory assigned to a person who makes deliveries

___ ___ ___ ___ ___ ___ ___ ___ ___ ___ ___ ___ ___ ___ ___ ___ ___
1 2 3 4 5 6 7 8 9 10 11 12 13 14 15 16 17

___ ___ ___ ___ ___ ___ ___ ___ ___ ___ ___. ___ ___ ___ ___ ___ ___ ___
18 19 20 21 22 23 24 25 26 27 28 29 30 31 32 33 34 35

___ ___ ___ ___ ___ ___ ___ ___ ___ ___ ___ ___. ___ ___ ___ ___ ___ ___
36 37 38 39 40 41 42 43 44 45 46 47 48 49 50 51 52 53

___ ___ ___ ___ ___ ___ ___ ___ ___ ___ ___ ___ ___ ___ ___ ___ ___. ___ ___
54 55 56 57 58 59 60 61 62 63 64 65 66 67 68 69 70 71 72

___ ___ ___ ___ ___ ___ ___ ___ ___ ___ ___ ___ ___ ___
73 74 75 76 77 78 79 80 81 82 83 84 85 86

___ ___ ___ ___ ___ ___ ___ ___ ___ ___ ___ ___ ___ ___ ___ ___ ___.
87 88 89 90 91 92 93 94 95 96 97 98 99 100 101 102 103

Unit 3

The Good Earth

As you read in the last unit, one question that mankind has often asked is, "What will the future bring?" Many people living in the last half of the twentieth century are asking this question in relation to our natural environment—the land on which we live. In this unit, the readings explore various attitudes toward the earth in general and more specifically toward our natural resources.

"A Fable for Tomorrow," the reading for Lesson 11, describes the efforts of Rachel Carson, a famous American biologist and author, to warn us about what may happen if we are not more careful in protecting the earth against environmental pollution.

"Life on Earth," the reading for Lesson 12, explains the concept of ecology and explores the relationships between living things and their environment. The authors describe the need for all of us to become more aware of how our actions affect the natural environment.

But just how to adapt our needs and desires to the needs of our natural environment is not a simple matter. In the reading for Lesson 13, "The Good Earth: Two Points of View," two experts on our natural resources discuss this complex problem.

Lessons 14 and 15 feature the American short story "Antaeus" in which the main character encounters resistance as he attempts to express his special love for the good earth.

Lesson 11

A Fable for Tomorrow

Words for Study

abundance	withered	substantial	toxic
maladies	vegetation	specter	pallbearers
moribund	anglers	marine	interior
pollination	granular	malaria	contamination

A Fable for Tomorrow

There was once a town in the heart of America where all life seemed to live in harmony with its surroundings. The town lay in the midst of a checkerboard of prosperous farms, with fields of grain and hillsides of orchards where, in spring, white clouds of bloom drifted above the green fields. In autumn, oak and maple and birch set up a blaze of color that flamed and flickered across a backdrop of pines. Then foxes barked in the hills and deer silently crossed the fields, half hidden in the mists of the fall mornings.

Along the roads laurel, viburnum and alder, great ferns and wildflowers delighted the traveler's eye through much of the year. Even in winter the roadsides were places of beauty, where countless birds came to feed on the berries and on the seed heads of the dried weeds rising above the snow. The countryside was, in fact, famous for the abundance and variety of its bird life, and when the flood of migrants was pouring through in spring and fall people traveled from great distances to observe them. Others came to fish the streams, which flowed clear and cold out of the hills and contained shady pools where trout lay. So it had been from the days many years ago when the first settlers raised their houses, sank their wells, and built their barns.

Then a strange blight crept over the area and everything began to change. Some evil spell had settled on the community: mysterious maladies swept the flocks of chickens; the cattle and sheep sickened and died. Everywhere was a shadow of death. The farmers spoke of much illness among their families. In the town the doctors had become more and more puzzled by new kinds of sickness appearing among their patients. There had been several sudden and unexplained deaths, not only among adults but even among children, who would be stricken suddenly while at play and die within a few hours.

There was a strange stillness. The birds, for example—where had they gone? Many people spoke of them, puzzled and disturbed. The feeding stations in the backyards were deserted. The few birds seen anywhere were moribund; they trembled violently and could not fly. It was a spring without voices. On the mornings that had once throbbed with the dawn chorus of robins, catbirds, doves, jays, wrens, and scores of other bird voices there was now no sound; only silence lay over the fields and woods and marsh.

On the farms the hens brooded, but no chicks hatched. The farmers complained that they were unable to raise any pigs—the litters were small and the young survived only a few days. The apple trees were coming into bloom but no bees droned among the blossoms, so there was no pollination and there would be no fruit.

The roadsides, once so attractive, were now lined with browned and withered vegetation as though swept by fire. These, too, were silent, deserted by all living things. Even the streams were now lifeless. Anglers no longer visited them, for all the fish had died.

In the gutters under the eaves and between the shingles of the roofs, a white granular powder still showed a few patches; some weeks before it had fallen like snow upon the roofs and the lawns, the fields and streams.

No witchcraft, no enemy action had silenced the rebirth of new life in this stricken world. The people had done it themselves.

This town does not actually exist, but it might easily have a thousand counterparts in America or elsewhere in the world. I know of no community that has experienced all the misfortunes I describe. Yet every one of these disasters has actually happened somewhere, and many real communities have already suffered a substantial number of them. A grim specter has crept upon us almost unnoticed, and this imagined tragedy may easily become a stark reality as we all shall know.

What has already silenced the voices of spring in countless towns in America? This book is an attempt to explain.

* * *

The author of "A Fable for Tomorrow" is Rachel Carson, an American biologist and writer. She is famous for her books on environmental pollution and on the natural history of the sea. The book to which she refers is *Silent Spring* which was published in 1962. The fable is the first chapter of this widely read book.

Rachel Carson's own story begins in Springdale, Pennsylvania, where she was born in the spring of 1907. The woods around her childhood home were where young Rachel first came into contact with the natural world that she was to defend all her life.

Wanting to become a writer, Miss Carson entered Pennsylvania State College for Women. When she took a required biology course, she decided that subject appealed to her more. Later she received her masters degree in biology from Johns Hopkins University and then studied marine biology at the Woods Hole Marine Biological Laboratory. Despite a long-felt love for the sea, Rachel Carson had never even seen a sea until she studied at Woods Hole, which is located on the Massachusetts coast.

The desire to write was still strong, however, and so after she finished her studies, she applied for a job with the United States Bureau of Fisheries as a writer and editor for its publications. She got the job and served with this agency for many years.

Her first book, *Under the Sea Wind*, was published on the eve of America's entry into World War II. Although the book did not sell well at the time, it was later reprinted and achieved great success.

It was during the war that Miss Carson had an opportunity to read many reports on scientific discoveries then being made. These reports included studies on substances used for pesticides, of which the best-known was DDT. DDT is the shortened form of dichloro-diphenyl-trichloro-ethane. Even as DDT was achieving its great breakthrough in combating malaria and other human diseases carried by insects, Rachel Carson was having serious second thoughts about the biological effects of DDT's widespread use. But her involvement during the wartime and postwar years was again with the sea.

In 1951 her second book, *The Sea Around Us*, was published and became a top best seller. Suddenly the little-known Rachel Carson was a national celebrity. She hated it. A quiet person, she wanted mainly to be left alone to work and write. But even though the success of *The Sea Around Us* brought her unwanted fame, it did give her the financial security she needed to make writing a full-time career.

It was in the 1950s that Rachel Carson was beginning to wonder what she might write to warn about the harm that mankind was doing to the earth. Some scientists had expressed doubts as early as 1945 about the effects of DDT on the environment. Later, facts about DDT's ability to accumulate in fatty tissue of wildlife started to emerge. Houseflies were becoming immune to DDT. Birds that ate insects sprayed with DDT died. Scientists gradually became aware of the fact that they did not really know what the long-term effects of DDT might be. It was an area that cried out for scientific investigation.

On the other hand, DDT was cheap, plentiful, and effective for the purposes of controlling insects. Farmers, especially, used it in vast quantities. One of its "advantages" was that it persisted in its toxic state for many years, so that farmers needed to use it only occasionally. And of course, as we now know, this was the most serious disadvantage of DDT—it continues to be with us, with its harmful effects as well as its benefits, for years.

Rachel Carson started what became an effort of several years to gather all the scientific information available about chemical pesticides and insecticides. When her book was finally published in 1962 as *Silent Spring*, it drew an unbelievable amount of criticism from the chemical industry and from the Department of Agriculture. Nearly all the criticism was based on either a failure to read the book or a deliberate attempt to distort what Rachel Carson had actually written.

Critics of *Silent Spring* said, for example, that it called for the end of all insecticide use. It did not. Rachel Carson was roundly and frequently criticized as having dabbled in the field of science where she had no right to dabble. This particular criticism was indeed strange, for Rachel Carson was a respected biologist and *Silent Spring* contains the most careful records of the work of many hundreds of scientists.

Dr. Norman E. Borlaug, winner of a Nobel Peace Prize for his work in developing new strains of wheat, asserted that *Silent Spring* had failed to mention the importance of chemicals in producing and protecting food and fiber crops.

Yet Miss Carson had written: "All this is not to say there is no insect problem and no need of control. I am saying, rather, that control must be geared to realities, not to mythical situations, and that the methods employed must be such that they do not destroy us along with the insects...

"It is not my contention that chemical insecticides must never be used. I do contend that we have put poisonous and biologically potent chemicals indiscriminately into the hands of persons largely or wholly ignorant of their potential for harm.

"We have subjected enormous numbers of people to contact with these poisons, without their consent and often without their knowledge. If the Bill of Rights contains no guarantee that a citizen shall be secure against lethal poisons distributed either by private individuals or by public officials, it is surely only because our forefathers, despite their considerable wisdom and foresight, could conceive of no such problem.

"I contend, furthermore, that we have allowed these chemicals to be used with little or no advance investigation of their effect on soil, water, wildlife and man himself. Future generations are unlikely to condone our lack of prudent concern for the integrity of the natural world that supports all life."

Few of her readers, friends and critics alike, knew what a physical effort it had been for Rachel Carson to write *Silent Spring*. While the book was being debated up and down the land, giving birth to some forty pieces of state legislation to limit the use of pesticides, its author became increasingly ill. By the summer of 1963, Rachel Carson knew she was dying. Few people realized that she was sick because she tried to carry on the defense of her ideas. Her last public appearance was to testify before a subcommittee of the Senate headed by Connecticut's Senator Abraham Ribicoff. The topic was suggestions for the proper use of pesticides.

Rachel Carson died in the spring of 1964. Among the pallbearers at her funeral were Secretary of the Interior Stewart Udall and Senator Ribicoff. The Senator called Rachel Carson "this gentle lady who aroused people everywhere to be concerned with one of the most significant problems of mid-20th century life—man's contamination of his environment."

1 **Understanding the Reading.** Write the letter of the best answer on the line to the left.

_____ 1. "A Fable for Tomorrow" appears in _____.

(a) *The Sea Around Us* (c) *The Edge of the Sea*
(b) *Silent Spring* (d) *Under the Sea Wind*

_____ 2. In the sentence "...and when the flood of migrants was pouring through in the spring and fall people traveled from great distances to see them," *migrants* refers to _____.

(a) birds (c) tourists
(b) fish (d) workers

_____ 3. The "strange blight" mentioned in "A Fable for Tomorrow" refers to _____.

(a) DDT (c) pollination
(b) malaria (d) witchcraft

_____ 4. Which word *least* describes the countryside after the "strange stillness"?

(a) moribund (c) substantial
(b) scenic (d) withered

_____ 5. Miss Carson probably wrote "A Fable for Tomorrow" _____.

(a) to emphasize how forces exist that are beyond our understanding
(b) to fulfill her ambitions as a writer
(c) to portray man's ability to destroy his environment
(d) to show what has happened to many American communities

_____ 6. When Miss Carson's findings on pesticides and insecticides were published, they were _____.

(a) instantly dismissed (c) universally praised
(b) severely criticized (d) generally ignored

_____ 7. Which of these statements about DDT is false?

(a) DDT is an effective combatant against many diseases.
(b) DDT was first used during World War II.
(c) Miss Carson was the first scientist to recognize the dangers of DDT.
(d) The toxic effect of DDT persists for many years.

_____ 8. Which word best describes Miss Carson's personal habits?

(a) carefree (c) reclusive
(b) inconsistent (d) sociable

_____ 9. Which of the following best indicates that Miss Carson succeeded in convincing people of the harm they are doing to the environment?

(a) Abraham Ribicoff's statement
(b) Dr. Borlaug's assertion
(c) forty pieces of state legislation
(d) testifying before the Senate subcommittee

2 **What Do You Think?** The following statement was made by Chief Seattle, a North American Indian. Read his statement and then answer the questions which follow in good sentence form. Be sure to offer reasons or examples to support your point of view.

> "Whatever befalls the earth befalls the sons of the earth. If men spit upon the ground, they spit on themselves. This we know—the earth does not belong to man, man belongs to the earth. All things are connected like the blood which unites one family. Whatever befalls the earth befalls the sons of the earth. Man did not weave the web of life; he is merely a strand in it. Whatever he does to the web, he does to himself."

1. Does Chief Seattle's statement support or contradict "A Fable for Tomorrow"? Explain.

____

____

____

2. Cite two things many Americans commonly do which suggest that they would agree with Chief Seattle's statement.

   a. ____

   b. ____

3. Cite two things many Americans commonly do which suggest that they would *not* agree with Chief Seattle's statement.

   a. ____

   b. ____

4. What is your reaction to Chief Seattle's statement?

____

____

____

____

3 **What Is the Nobel Prize?** It was mentioned in the reading that one of Miss Carson's critics had won a Nobel Prize. Use the words listed at the left to complete this information about these prizes.

anniversary
distinction
economics
enrichment
substantial

1. Awarded each year on December 10, the ________________ of Alfred Nobel's death, the Nobel Prizes are given to men and women who have achieved ________________ in the fields of medicine, physics, literature, chemistry, peace, and ________________, and have made a ________________ contribution for the ________________ of humanity.

accumulated
distinguished
estate
massive
portion

2. Born in Sweden in 1833, Alfred Nobel was a ________________ inventor who ________________ a ________________ fortune from the manufacture of dynamite and other explosives. When he died in 1896, he left the major ________________ of his ________________ (about $8.5 million) for the institution of the Nobel Prizes.

abundance
capable
fateful
incident
tragedy

3. Nobel's innovations in the field of explosives brought him an ________________ of wealth, but they also brought him personal ________________. One ________________ day in 1864, for example, just after the ________________ chemist had begun making nitroglycerin, the factory blew up. Nobel's youngest brother and four others were killed in this disastrous ________________.

determinedly
indignant
minimize
rebuild
reliable

4. Vigorously denounced by ________________ Swedes as a "mad scientist" and public enemy, and forbidden to ________________ his factory, Nobel ________________ continued his experiments on a barge, seeking a ________________ way to ________________ the danger of handling nitroglycerin.

ambitions
ample
dedicated
exertion
inevitable

5. Many will concur that no matter how __________ a person is in pursuing his __________, it is more often than not an __________ dose of good fortune rather than personal __________ that makes success __________.

discredited
patents
precisely
reclusive
sociable

6. And this is __________ what happened in the case of Alfred Nobel who, through a chance discovery, perfected the explosive he named dynamite for which he was granted exclusive __________ in 1867 and 1868. The man who had been __________ as a "mad scientist" was now rich and famous. The fame, at least, must have burdened Nobel who was __________ rather than __________ by nature.

4 **Names in Nature.** Choose the best answers for these brief word histories.

_____ 1. This plant got its name because, as Captain John Smith wrote in 1624, "The Poysoned weed is much in shape like our English ivy."
(a) dandelion (b) poison ivy (c) poison oak (d) ragweed

_____ 2. The ancient Roman colony Tarentum gave its name to this fearsome-looking, hairy bug.
(a) moth (b) tarantula (c) tick (d) yellow jacket

_____ 3. The explorer Hernando de Soto didn't realize this animal was actually a bison when he gave it the Spanish name meaning "wild ox" in 1544.
(a) antelope (b) buffalo (c) bull (d) steer

_____ 4. First recorded in 1682, this animal's name also comes from the Spanish—*el lagarto*, which means lizard.
(a) alligator (b) crocodile (c) Gila monster (d) turtle

_____ 5. From two Spanish words, both of which mean "having no master" comes the name of this wild, or half-wild animal.
(a) burro (b) camel (c) mustang (d) muskrat

_____ 6. Named after the garden herb, this is so abundant in the western plains that by 1894 it became the nickname for the state of Nevada.
(a) cactus (b) crabgrass (c) sagebrush (d) tumbleweed

_____ 7. This word derived from the French means "large meadow."
(a) glen (b) prairie (c) range (d) valley

_____ 8. The first major Louisiana French word to enter American English, this word—which the French borrowed from the Choctaw Indians—means "creek."
(a) bayou (b) bog (c) delta (d) stream

_____ 9. From the Greek word meaning "sprout," our 18th-century ancestors referred to this vegetable as "sparrow-grass."
(a) artichoke (b) asparagus (c) broccoli (d) cauliflower

_____ 10. When this bird was discovered, it was named after certain officials in the Roman Catholic Church because its color was the same as their hats.
(a) blackbird (b) blue jay (c) cardinal (d) yellowthroat

5 **The Good Earth.** Look at the map below to see into what regions the earth is divided. Then examine the bar graph. This graph includes two pieces of information for each of the eight regions of the world found on the map. For each region, the graph tells what percentage of soil is suited to growing crops and what percentage of soil is actually used to grow crops. When you have examined the graph, do **Part A** and **Part B**.

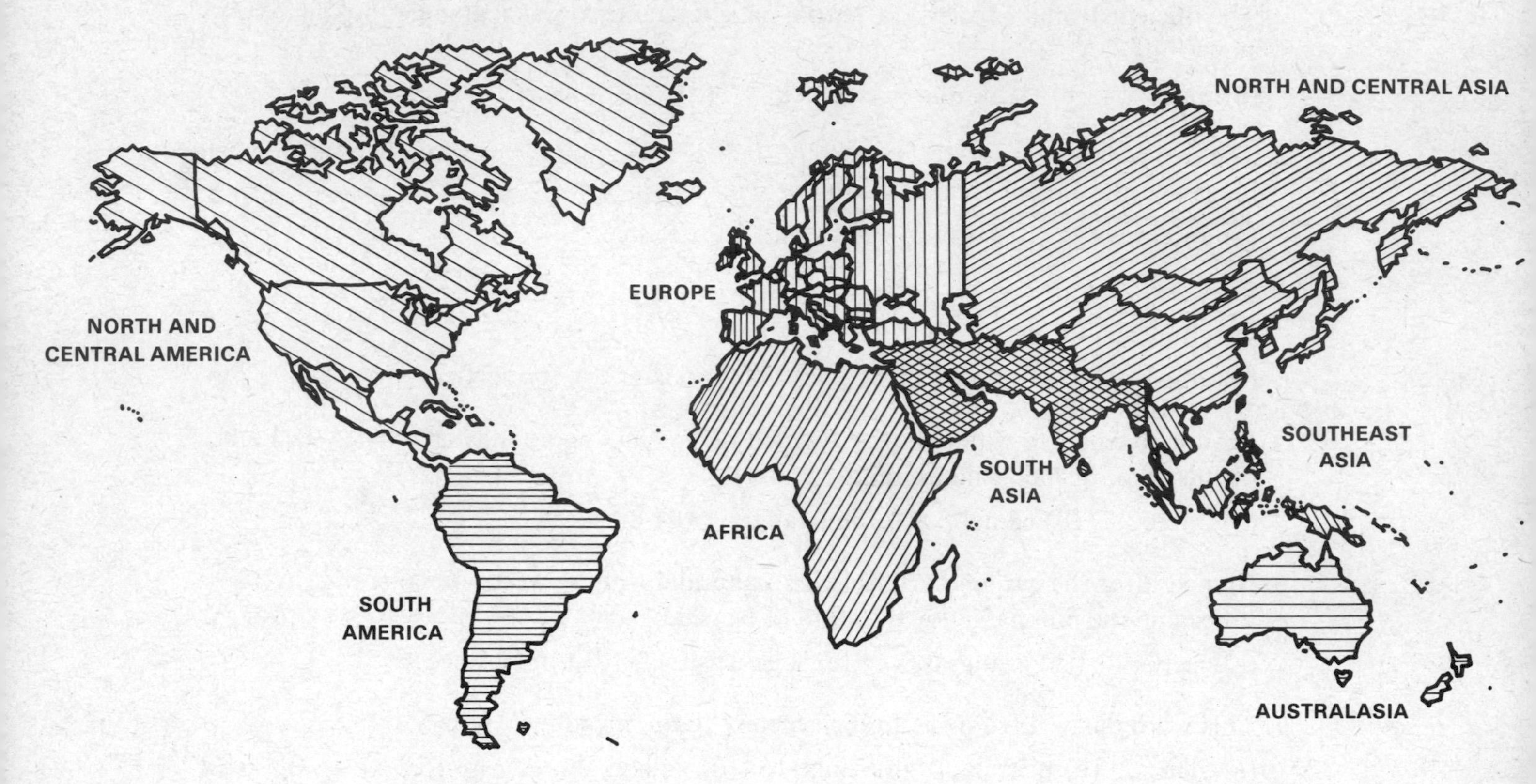

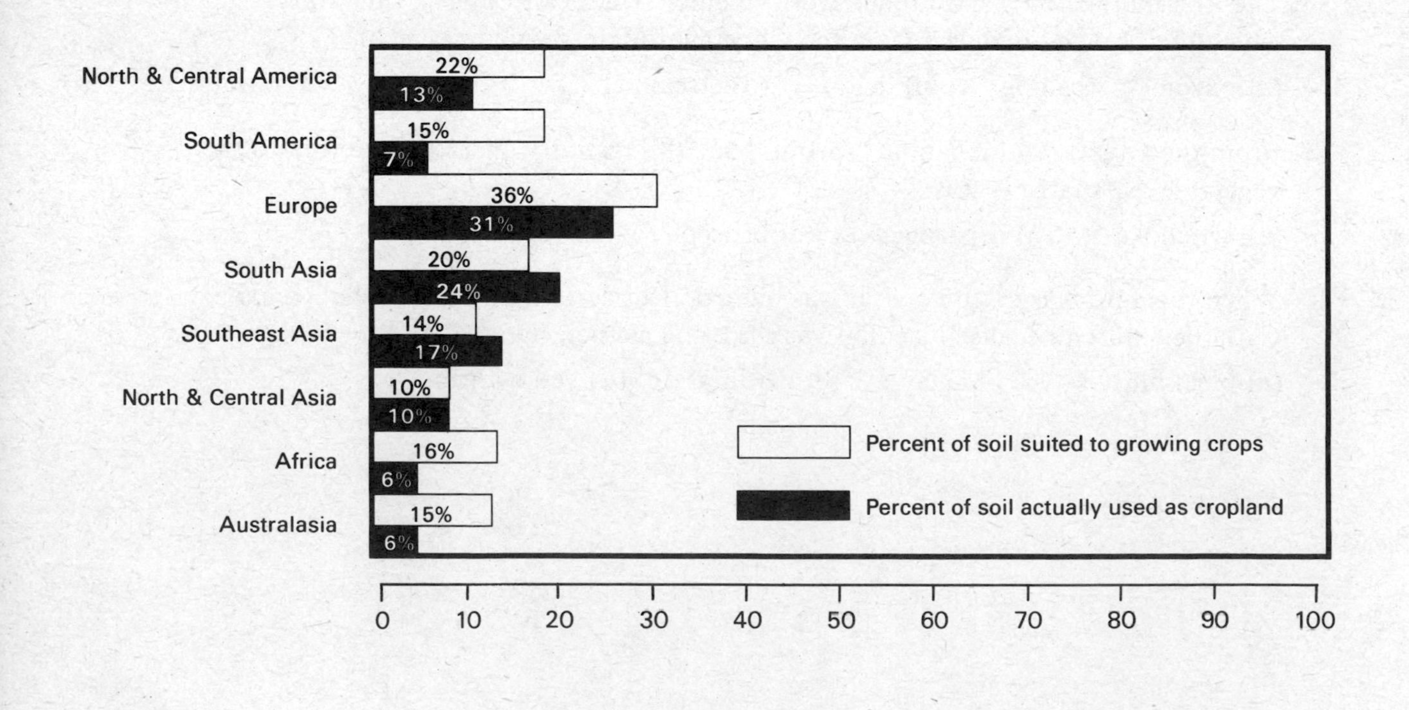

Graph based on information from *Gaia: An Atlas of Planet Management* edited by Dr. Norman Myers.

Part A. Read the statements below. If a statement is true based on the information on the graph, write **T** on the line to the left. If it is false, write **F**. Write a **?** if the answer cannot be determined from the information on the graph.

_____ 1. In South America, more soil is suitable for growing crops than is actually used for this purpose.

_____ 2. In Southeast Asia, more soil is actually used for growing crops than is suited for this purpose.

_____ 3. In North and Central Asia, more soil is suitable for growing crops than is actually used for this purpose.

_____ 4. South Asia contains a greater percentage of soil suited to growing crops than does Southeast Asia.

_____ 5. Europe contains more square miles of land suitable for growing crops than South America does.

_____ 6. Of the eight areas of the world noted on the graph, North and Central Asia has the smallest percentage of soil suited to growing crops.

_____ 7. North and Central Americans use a greater percentage of their soil for growing crops than South Asians.

_____ 8. Africa contains a smaller percentage of soil suited to growing crops than does Europe because Africa has more desert than Europe.

_____ 9. Nearly one-third of the land in Europe is used to grow crops.

_____ 10. In South Asia, some people are trying to grow crops on soil that is *not* suited to this purpose.

Part B. Now decide what conclusions can reasonably be drawn using the information on the graph and your own background knowledge. If you think a statement is reasonable, write **R** on the line to the left; if you think it is not reasonable, write **N**.

_____ 1. North and Central America contain enough soil suitable for growing crops to keep the current population from starving.

_____ 2. People in Southeast Asia probably try to grow crops on soil not suited for this purpose because there are so many people to feed.

_____ 3. In Africa, people are starving because there is not enough soil suitable for growing crops.

_____ 4. By the year 2222, people in North and Central Asia will probably have to try to grow crops on soil not suited for this purpose in order to have enough food.

_____ 5. If the population of Australasia increases, the people will soon run out of soil suitable for growing crops.

_____ 6. In Europe, a greater percentage of the soil is devoted to growing crops than in other parts of the world because Europeans do not grow crops as efficiently as people in other parts of the world.

Lesson 12

Life on Earth

Words for Study

ecosystem	predatory	estuaries	exploiting
niche	prey	sediment	ruthless
radiations	capacity	brackish	erosion
predation	habitat	radiant	unique
competition	microorganism	parasite	capabilities

Life on Earth

The word *ecology* was first defined by the German biologist Ernst Haeckel in 1869. He described ecology as the study of relationships between living things and the environment in which they live. Ecologists view the animal and plant populations within a given area as a *community* in which different organisms perform different roles. A community of living things, together with the non-living parts of their environment, forms what is called an *ecosystem.*

The whole earth is one large ecosystem; a forest, an ocean, a pond, and a rotting log are smaller ecosystems. The living things in any ecosystem can be classified according to their functions. The *producers* are the green plants, which make food. The *consumers* are the animals, which eat plants or other animals. The *decomposers* are the bacteria and other tiny organisms that break down animal wastes and the remains of dead plants and animals into raw materials. These raw materials are used by the plants to make more food.

Each species of organism in the ecosystem has a specific task: each plant species produces a different kind of food, each animal consumes different food, and each decomposer performs a different operation on the wastes. Ecologists call a species' task its *niche.* If two species compete for the same niche in an ecosystem, one species or the other eventually dies out.

All these living things are constantly affecting and being affected by each other, as well as by the non-living things in their environment—the soil, the water, and the air. Everything in nature is constantly changing—usually very gradually, but sometimes rapidly—so no ecosystem can remain completely stable over a long period of time.

The *physical*, or non-living, environmental factors in an ecosystem include the light, temperature, radiations, pressure, water, air, climate, gravity, and soil. For each of these factors the organisms have minimum and maximum acceptable values in the environment in which they live. For example, the maximum temperature an animal can endure is about 126° F.

The *biological* factors in an ecosystem are even more complex than the physical factors. Two important biological factors that tend to limit animal populations are *predation* and *competition.* Predation is the killing of animals by other animals for food. Predatory animals are usually much fewer in number than the animals they prey on, and their hunting helps to keep the prey animals from increasing beyond the capacity of their food supply.

Competition is the striving of two or more organisms for a necessity of life such as food, water, minerals, living space, or sunlight for plants. Competition occurs when there is not enough of one or more of these necessities to fill the needs of all.

The part of the ecosystem where an organism lives is called its *habitat.* A fish's habitat could be a whole pond; a microorganism's habitat might be a tiny area on the pond floor. One of the most

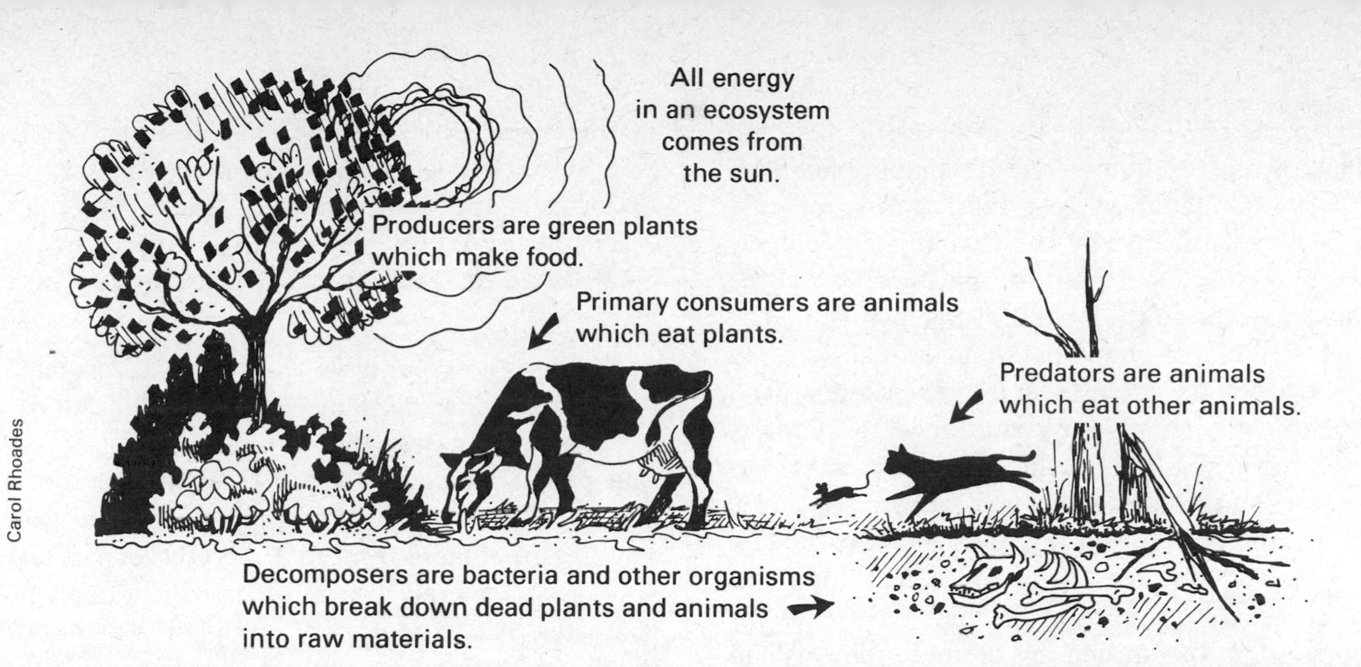

unusual habitats is the cave, which accommodates different animal and plant species in an environment of almost total darkness.

The forest, with its abundance of trees of different heights, bushes, climbing vines, and so on, is one of the environments richest in plant and animal variety. Ecologically, it is one of the finest because the soil retains all its natural richness, and the water system is regulated by the trees and smaller plants. The forest is a genuine "explosion" of vitality. It provides an ideal habitat for the most widely different species of living things, with all kinds of living habits. Unfortunately, humans have destroyed many forests and converted the land to farms.

Another habitat that is rich in living organisms is marshes, or wetlands. Here, organisms form in the shallow parts of a lake where water plants can take root and multiply. They also form along rivers in places where the land is too flat for the water to drain off. Organisms especially favor estuaries—the places where rivers slow down and deposit their sediment before emptying into the sea. Estuaries are referred to as tidal marshes because the tide pushes salty ocean water into the marsh twice a day.

Tidal marshes are filled with plants that are adapted to both salt water and the brackish fresh water left when the tide ebbs. Many ocean fishes, crabs, lobsters, and so on lay their eggs in tidal marshes, where the plants and their varied insect populations provide food for the young sea animals when they hatch. These "nurseries of the ocean" contain many times as much living material as the open sea.

Only recently has the value of wetlands been recognized and an effort made to keep them from being filled in with rubbish and soil as sites for homes or factories.

All of the energy in an ecosystem comes originally from the sun. By drying and weighing all the plants from a measured area of land, scientists can estimate how much of the radiant energy reaching the area has been changed by green plants into chemical energy, or food. Some of that energy is transferred to the prime consumers—grazing mammals, birds, insects, and even parasite plants that feed on the green plants. Finally, some of the energy reaches the bacteria and other microorganisms as they decompose the wastes and remains of the plants and animals.

Energy cannot be destroyed; but whenever it is used, some is changed into heat and transferred to the surrounding air, where it is no longer available to power the growth or activities of living organisms.

A portion of the energy stored in the green plant is used and lost in this way by each organism in the *food chain*. The food chain includes the plant itself, the prime consumer, the one or more predators in the chain, and the decomposers. Thus the population of any species of organism in the food chain is limited by the energy available to it from other organisms in the food chain on which it feeds.

Human beings are no exception to this rule. Since our ancestors learned to raise plants and animals for food about ten thousand years ago, the human population has been growing—slowly at first, but at an ever-increasing rate.

In the two hundred years between 1650 and 1850 the earth's human population doubled from five hundred million to a billion. This increase was made possible by the development of new ways to raise food crops, of machines to use the energy stored in the earth's deposits of coal, gas, and oil, and of ways to extend human lives by curing certain diseases and preventing others. Such developments have continued to increase, making possible a world population that was nearly four billion in 1977 and growing at a rate that could double that figure by the year 2000.

Man's need for living space and food has increased in proportion to the increase in his population. In addition, his desire for objects and services that can only be provided by exploiting the earth's limited supply of forest, stored minerals, and stored energy has sky rocketed over the past hundred years.

To satisfy these needs and desires, we have been trespassing more and more on natural areas, destroying their plant and animal populations as we grow. In the past century, for example, the millions of bison that once roamed the North American prairies have been reduced by ruthless hunting to a few small herds that would disappear without human efforts to keep them alive. Many species of whales—the earth's biggest mammals—have been hunted to near-extinction and will not survive unless all nations forbid their destruction. Many other species of mammals, birds, and fish have been destroyed or require an intense human will and effort to insure their survival.

In many parts of the world the destruction of forests for farming, timber, and fuel have left immense areas without plant cover, exposed to continuous erosion by wind and water. Fortunately, more than a hundred years ago, some far-sighted persons realized the importance of preserving at least some natural areas. Thus was born the world's first national park, Yellowstone, in Montana, Idaho, and Wyoming. Many more such parks have since been established in the United States and other countries.

At first these parks were set aside to protect the wild animals and plants from humans and to serve as "showcases" for visitors. The hope was that people would develop a respect for nature and an understanding of its processes. Scientists now realize that our need to preserve natural areas is not merely beautiful or educational in character. The extinction of any plant or animal species withdraws its unique genes from the earth's "gene bank"—genes that scientists might use to develop new and better breeds of plants and animals for human needs.

Man's ability to change the environment to suit his needs and desires is an important reason for the immense growth of the human population. But we have been pouring our waste gases, liquids, solids, and heat—many of them toxic to living organisms including ourselves—into the earth's atmosphere, waters, and soil without regard for the capacity of natural forces to make the wastes harmless or useful as raw materials.

In this way we have polluted the physical part of our environment and thus threatened our own survival as well as that of other living things. Furthermore, we have only recently recognized that our supply of fossil fuels—energy from the sun that was stored underground in plant and animal remains of millions of years ago and gradually converted into coal, oil, and natural gas—is not endless. It seems clear that we must adapt our behavior to the requirements and capabilities of our natural environment, if man is to continue being a "successful" species.

1

Understanding the Reading: Part 1. Write the letter of the best answer on the line to the left.

______ 1. According to ecologists, a *community* is ______.
(a) a defined area in which plants and animals live
(b) an ecosystem
(c) the relationship between living things and their environment
(d) the relationship between living things and their function

______ 2. In an ecosystem, living things are grouped in categories according to their ______.
(a) environment (b) function (c) importance (d) size

______ 3. Corn is classified as a(n) ______.
(a) consumer (b) decomposer (c) ecosystem (d) producer

______ 4. The ______ provide corn and other plants with raw materials.
(a) animals (b) decomposers (c) consumers (d) producers

______ 5. In this reading selection *habitat* means ______.
(a) biological factor (b) climate (c) competition (d) locality

______ 6. The inevitable result of two species striving for the same niche is the ______ of one of the species.
(a) death (b) migration (c) overpopulation (d) relaxation

______ 7. Predatory animals contribute to an ecosystem in that their activities partly solve the problem of ______.
(a) community (b) death (c) migration (d) overpopulation

______ 8. Which of the following is *not* a true statement about wetlands?
(a) A synonym for wetland is *marsh*.
(b) Wetlands are found in flat rather than mountainous regions.
(c) People have long recognized the value of this habitat.
(d) Some consider the wetlands to be a favorable site for construction.

______ 9. Which of the following is a true statement about energy?
(a) If energy isn't conserved properly, it is destroyed.
(b) Most of our energy originates deep inside the earth.
(c) The decomposers change the sun's energy into chemical energy.
(d) The population of a species is determined by the amount of energy available to it.

______ 10. In the food chain, human beings are classified as ______.
(a) consumers (b) decomposers (c) predators (d) producers

2 **Understanding the Reading: Part 2.** Answer the following questions in good sentence form. Be sure to include information from the reading to support your answers.

1. Cite two factors that have contributed to the rapid increase in world population.

   a. ____

   ____

   b. ____

   ____

2. What impact has increased world population had upon our natural resources?

   ____

   ____

   ____

   ____

3. What reason do the authors offer for their assertion: "...we must adapt our behavior to the requirements and capabilities of our natural environment, if man is to continue being a 'successful' species"?

   ____

   ____

   ____

What do you think? Do you think we are doing enough to "adapt our behavior to the requirements and capabilities of our natural environment" to continue to be a successful species? Explain.

____

____

____

____

____

____

____

3 **Synonyms and Antonyms.** Choose a synonym to fill in the first blank in each sentence. Choose an antonym to fill in the second blank.

Synonyms		Antonyms	
abundant	intricate	deny	needy
affirm	prosperous	develop	purify
contaminate	radiant	drowsy	simple
decompose	ruthless	dull	skimpy
dismiss	vigorous	employ	strife
harmony	withered	merciful	thriving

1. Ample and ________________ are antonyms for ________________.
2. Complicated and ________________ are antonyms for ________________.
3. Decay and ________________ are antonyms for ________________.
4. Discharge and ________________ are antonyms for ________________.
5. Energetic and ________________ are antonyms for ________________.
6. Agreement and ________________ are antonyms for ________________.
7. Pollute and ________________ are antonyms for ________________.
8. Profess and ________________ are antonyms for ________________.
9. Savage and ________________ are antonyms for ________________.
10. Shriveled and ________________ are antonyms for ________________.
11. Sparkling and ________________ are antonyms for ________________.
12. Thriving and ________________ are antonyms for ________________.

4 **Charting Information.** Scientists have grouped the *consumers* in the food chain into five basic categories:

1. **Herbivores.** These consumers eat plants only.
2. **Carnivores.** These consumers are meat eaters.
3. **Omnivores.** These consumers normally eat both plants and animals.
4. **Scavengers.** These consumers eat dead animals of all species, including their own species.
5. **Parasites.** These consumers are not able to obtain their food independently, but must live in or on other living organisms called **hosts.**

Use an encyclopedia or dictionary and the process of elimination to help you correctly place on the chart the organisms listed below.

bears	crocodiles	grasshoppers	human beings	ticks
buzzards	fleas	hippopotamuses	sharks	vultures

Consumers in the Food Chain

Herbivores	Carnivores	Omnivores
________	________	________
________	________	________

Scavengers	Parasites
________	________
________	________

5

Spelling Check. The word *niche* not only refers to a species' task; it can also refer to a place, employment, or activity that is specially suited to a person's ability or character. Can you identify the people who would best fill the niches described below?

- Fill in the answers by using all the syllables in the box. Use each syllable only once. The number after each description tells you how many syllables are in the word. The first one is done to get you started.
- When the words are correctly filled in, their first letters, reading down, will reveal the name of a well-known Englishman who is praised for his efforts in conserving natural resources.

aoh	cian	con	cor	dy	er	et	field	form	gist	grant
hyp	im	in	in	ist	la	land	mi	mol	ner	no	non	o
o	✓ot	✓pa	Phar	phy	rogue	si	struc	tist	tor	✓tri	y

p a t r i o t — 1. This person's niche is supporting and defending his country. (3)

_ _ _ _ _ — 2. This person's niche is playing mischievous tricks on others. (1)

_ _ _ _ _ _ _ _ _ — 3. This person hopes to find his niche by settling in another country. (3)

_ _ _ _ _ _ _ _ _ _ _ _ _ — 4. This person's niche is disregarding the accepted rules of society. (4)

_ _ _ _ _ _ _ — 5. This person's niche is investigating deaths which don't seem natural. (3)

_ _ _ _ _ _ _ _ _ _ _ — 6. This person's niche is researching the origin and history of words. (5)

_ _ _ _ _ _ _ _ _ — 7. This person's niche is an examining room. (3)

_ _ _ _ _ _ _ _ _ — 8. This person's niche is making suggestions after putting you in trance. (3)

_ _ _ _ _ _ _ _ _ — 9. This person's niche is cutting off line drives and making double plays. (3)

_ _ _ _ _ _ _ _ — 10. This woman's niche is renting apartments. (3)

_ _ _ _ _ _ _ _ _ _ — 11. This person's niche is the classroom. (3)

_ _ _ _ _ _ _ — 12. This person's niche used to be ruling ancient Egypt. (2)

The name of the British conservationist: P _ _ _ _ _   _ _ _ _ _ _

Lesson 13

The Good Earth: Two Points of View

Words for Study

cascade	penalizing	accessible	corrugated
lode	consolation	abandoned	caches
transcendent	terrain	detritus	Arcadia
precedence	ravine	macabre	succulent
recommend	traversed	bestrewn	hydraulic

The Good Earth: Two Points of View

Most people will agree that measures need to be taken to conserve our precious natural resources. The question is—what measures should be taken?

The writer John McPhee once climbed the mountains in the Cascade Range, an area rich in copper which is situated in the Western United States. With him were two men whose ideas about the uses of natural resources were quite different. One of these men was David Brower, the leader of a conservation organization called Friends of the Earth. The other was Charles Park, a mineral engineer.

As you read Mr. McPhee's description of this expedition, notice the different viewpoints presented by Brower and Park.

* * *

Near the southern base of Plummer Mountain and in the deep valley between Plummer Mountain and Glacier Peak—that is, in the central foreground of the view that we were looking at from Cloudy Pass—was the lode of copper that Kennecott would mine, and to do so the company would make an open pit at least two thousand four hundred feet from rim to rim.

Park said, "A hole in the ground will not materially hurt this scenery."

Brower stood up. "None of the experts on scenic resources will agree with you," he said. "This is one of the few remaining great wildernesses in the lower forty-eight. Copper is not a transcendent value here."

"Without copper, we'd be in a pretty sorry situation."

"If that deposit didn't exist, we'd get by without it."

"I would prefer the mountain as it is, but the copper is there."

"If we're down to where we have to take copper from places this beautiful, we're down pretty far."

"Minerals are where you find them. The quantities are finite. It's criminal to waste minerals when the standard of living of your people depends upon them. A mine cannot move. It is fixed by nature. So it has to take precedence over any other use. If there were a copper deposit in Yellowstone Park, I'd recommend mining it. Proper use of minerals is essential. You have to go get them where they are. Our standard of living is based on this."

"For a fifty-year cycle, yes. But for the long term, no. We have to drop our standard of living, so that people a thousand years from now can have any standard of living at all."

A breeze coming off the nearby acres of snow felt cool but not chilling in the sunshine, and rumpled the white hair of the two men.

"I am not for penalizing people today for the sake of future generations," Park said.

"I really am," said Brower. "That's where we differ."

"Yes, that's where we disagree. In 1910, the Brazilian government said they were going to preserve the iron ore in Minas Gerais, because the earth would run short of it in the future. People—thousands and thousands of people in Minas Gerais—were actually starving, and they were living over one of the richest ore deposits in the world, a fifteen-billion-ton reserve. They're mining it now, and people there are prospering. But in the past it was poor consolation to people who were going hungry to say that in the future it was going to be better. You have to use these things when you have them. You have to know where they are, and use them. People, in the future, will go for the copper here."

"The kids who are in Congress in the future should make that decision, and if it's theirs to make I don't think they'll go for the copper here," Brower said.

"Sure they will. They'll have to, if people are going to expect to have telephones, electric lights, airplanes, television sets, radios, central heating, air-conditioning, automobiles. And you *know* people will want these things. I didn't invent them. I just know where the copper is."

Brower swung his pack up onto his back. "Pretend the copper deposit down there doesn't exist," he said. "Then what would you do? What are you going to do when it's gone?"

"You're trying to make everything wilderness," Park said.

"No, I'm not. I'm trying to keep at least two per cent of the terrain as wilderness."

"Two per cent is a lot."

"Two per cent is under pavement."

"Basically, our difference is that I feel we can't stop all this—we must direct it. You feel we must stop it."

"I feel we should go back, recycle, do things over again, and do better, even if it costs more. We mine things and don't use them again. We coat the surface of the earth—with beer cans and chemicals, asphalt and old television sets."

"We *are* recycling copper, but we don't have enough."

"When we knock buildings down, we don't take the copper out. Every building that comes down could be a copper mine. But we don't take the copper out. We go after fresh metal. We destroy that mountain."

"How can you ruin a mountain like Glacier Peak?" Park lifted his pick toward the mountain. "You *can't* ruin it," he went on, waving the pick. "Look at the Swiss mountains. Who could ruin *them*? A mine would not hurt this country—not with proper housekeeping."

Brower started on down the trail. We retrieved our packs and caught up with him. About five hundred feet below us and a mile ahead was another pass—Suiattle Pass—and to reach it we had to go down into a big ravine and up the other side. There were long silences, measured by the sound of boots on the trail. From time to time, the pick rang out against a rock.

Brower said, "Would America have to go without much to leave its wilderness unspoiled?"

We traversed a couple of switchbacks and approached the bottom of the ravine. Then Park said, "Where they are more easily accessible, deposits have been found and are being—or have been—mined."

We had seen such a mine near Lake Chelan, in the eastern part of the mountains. The Howe Sound Mining Company established an underground copper mine there in 1938, built a village and called it Holden. The Holden mine was abandoned in 1957. We had hiked past its remains on our way to the wilderness area. Against a backdrop of snowy peaks, two flat-topped hills of earth detritus broke the landscape. One was the dump where all the rock had been put that was removed before the miners reached the ore body. The other consisted of tailings—crushed rock that had been through the Holden mill and had yielded copper. What remained of the mill itself was a macabre skeleton of bent, twisted, rusted beams. Wooden buildings and sheds were rotting and gradually collapsing. The area was bestrewn with huge flakes of corrugated iron, rusted rails, rusted ore carts, old barrels. Although there was no way for an automobile to get to Holden except by barge up Lake Chelan and then on a dirt road to the village, we saw there a high pile of gutted and rusted automobiles, which themselves had originally been rock in the earth and, in the end, in Holden, were crumbling slowly back into the ground.

Park hit a ledge with the pick. We were moving up the other side of the ravine now. The going was steep, and the pace slowed. Brower said, "We saw that at Holden."

I counted twenty-two steps watching the backs of Brower's legs, above the red tops of gray socks. He was moving slower than I would have. I was close behind him. His legs, blue-veined, seemed less pink than they had the day before. They were sturdy but not athletically shapely. Brower used to put food caches in various places in the High Sierra and go from one to another for weeks at a time. He weighed two hundred and twelve pounds now, and he must have wished he were one-eighty.

Park said, "Holden is the sort of place that gave mining a bad name. This has been happening in the West for the past hundred years, but it doesn't have to happen. Poor housekeeping is poor housekeeping wherever you find it. I don't care if it's a mine or a kitchen. Traditionally, when mining companies finished in a place they just walked off. Responsible groups are not going to do that anymore. They're not going to leave trash; they're not going to deface the countryside. Think of that junk! If I had enough money, I'd come up here and clean it up."

I thought how neat Park's house, his lawn, and his gardens are—his roses, his lemon tree, his two hundred varieties of cactus. The name of the street he lives on is Arcadia Place. Park is a member of the Cactus and Succulent Society of America. He hit a fallen tree with the hammer end.

"It's one god-awful mess," Brower said.

"That old mill could be cleaned up," Park said. "Grass could be planted on the dump and the tailings."

Suiattle Pass was now less than a quarter mile ahead of us. I thought of Brower, as a child, on his first trip to the Sierra Nevada. His father drove him there from Berkeley in a 1916 Maxwell. On the western slopes, they saw both the aftermath and the actual operations of hydraulic mining for gold. Men with hoses eight inches in diameter directed water with such force against the hillsides that large parts of the hills themselves fell away as slurry.

"Holden was abandoned in 1957, and no plants of any kind have caught on the dump and the tailings," Brower said.

Holden, in its twenty years of metal production, brought out of the earth ten million tons of rock—enough to make a hundred thousand tons of copper, enough to wire Kansas City.

Park said, "You could put a little fertilizer on—something to get it started."

When we reached the pass, we stood for a moment and looked again at Glacier Peak and, far below us, the curving white line of the Suiattle. Park said, "When you create a mine, there are two things you can't avoid: a hole in the ground and a dump for waste rock. Those are two things you can't avoid."

Brower said, "Except by not doing it at all."

1 **Understanding the Reading.** Answer the following questions. Where appropriate, use good sentence form and information from the reading to support your answers.

1. With the help of context clues and a dictionary, write a brief definition for each of the italicized words below.

   a. "...we had to go down into a big *ravine* and up the other side."

   ____

   b. "We traversed a couple of *switchbacks*..."

   ____

   c. "...two flat-topped hills of earth *detritus* broke the landscape."

   ____

   d. "Men with hoses eight inches in diameter directed water with such force against the hillsides that large parts of the hills themselves fell away as *slurry*."

   ____

2. What is the setting for this reading? ______________________________

   ____

3. What is about to happen in this setting? ______________________________

   ____

4. What is David Brower's occupation? ______________________________

5. What is Charles Park's occupation? ______________________________

6. Why does Park use the example of Minas Gerais? ______________________________

   ____

   ____

   ____

   ____

7. Explain how Brower and Park agree in their comments about Holden.

   ____

   ____

   ____

   ____

8. Explain the basic disagreement between Brower and Park in their viewpoints on the uses of natural resources.

What do you think? What is your point of view about this discussion of natural resources?

2 **The Earth: A Cartoonist's Point of View.** Study the cartoon and answer the questions which follow.

1. How would David Brower probably respond to this cartoon?

____

____

2. How would Charles Park probably respond to this cartoon?

____

____

3. Describe your response to this cartoon.

____

____

3 **Word Families.** Use the words listed at the left to complete each sentence correctly.

vigor
vigorous

1. As the ______________ early American settlers worked to tame and exploit the American wilderness little did they realize that their great-grandchildren would, with equal ______________, have to resolve problems they had created.

prosper
prosperous
prosperity

2. "We cannot continue our style of ______________," claims a respected environmentalist, adding the warning that to ______________ at the expense of our precious resources is the least ______________ of courses in the long run.

consistent
inconsistent
consistently
consistency

3. "______________ is the key to self-mastery," another ______________ reminds audiences attending her lectures. "And it is tragic that we have been so ______________ in exploiting the land for our own selfish gain and so ______________ in our attempts to remedy this disastrous situation."

emphasize
emphasis
emphatic

4. It may be true that public education and the media ______________ environmental issues more than they ever have; but ecologists like David Brower are ______________ in their assertion that this ______________ isn't strong enough.

probable
improbable
probability

5. Even though ecologists stress the strong ______________ that we will exhaust our natural resources, many Americans assume this possibility to be ______________ because they believe that scientific solutions to environmental questions are highly ______________.

complicate
complicated
complication

6. Many ecologists agree that protecting the environment is further ______________ because the interests of different groups vary; these groups ______________ the basic issues and entangle environmental discussions in one ______________ after another.

4 **America's Resources.** Use a dictionary or other reference book to help you complete these descriptions of some of America's beautiful resources.

1. Located in southern ______________, the Everglades, one of the world's largest swamps, was uninhabited until the Seminole Indians fled to the area in 1842 after wars with U.S. troops and white settlers.

2. Niagara Falls consists of two main falls, the Canadian or ______________ Falls and the American Falls. In 1683 a Roman Catholic priest wrote: "These waters foam and boil in a fearful manner."

3. ______________, ______________, ______________, ______________, and ______________ form the largest group of freshwater lakes in the world. Called the Great Lakes, they occupy an area of 94,710 square miles on either side of the U.S.-Canadian boundary.

4. The Spanish explorer ______________ de Soto was the first European to travel on the Mississippi River. He crossed the river in 1541 while searching for gold. The word *Mississippi* comes from an Indian word meaning "big river."

5. Situated in the state of ______________, the Mesabi Range is a chain of hills which was once one of the great iron ore regions of the world. *Mesabi* is an Indian word meaning "hidden giant."

6. Situated in southwestern ______________ and northeastern Wyoming, the Sioux Indians called them the Black Hills because the pine forests covering the slopes looked black when seen from the plains. In these hills is the town of Lead, home of the largest gold mine in the United States.

7. In the year ______________ Congress established Yellowstone National Park. This is the oldest national park and is noted for its scenic beauty, wildlife, and geysers.

8. Located in northwestern ______________, Great Salt Lake is a natural wonder of the world. Although fed by freshwater streams, this inland sea is saltier than the ocean.

9. A gorge formed by the ______________ River, the Grand Canyon was named by John Wesley Powell, an American geologist who led an expedition through the vast canyon in 1869.

10. Located in central ______________, the Painted Desert is a brilliantly colored region extending about 200 miles along the Little Colorado River. This region is particularly beautiful at sunrise and sunset.

11. Located on the island of ______________, Mauna Loa is the world's largest volcano. Its longest eruption, which occurred in 1855-56, lasted for 18 months.

12. Named after ______________ McKinley, the twenty-fifth president of the United States, Mount McKinley is often called "the top of the continent" because it has the highest summit in North America. Mount McKinley is situated in central Alaska.

5 **Can You Crack the Code?** Copper is a valuable metal that was mentioned in the reading. Can you crack the code of this puzzle and identify some other valuable metals? The code is the same for all the metals. When you have guessed a metal, fill in the letters and use these letters for the other metals until you have cracked the code for the entire group. Use the facts about the metals to help you crack the code. The first one is done to get you started.

COPPER 1. A E Z Z T F	An excellent conductor of heat and electricity, this metal is widely used for electrical wiring and water piping.
2. K E D J	One of the first known metals, the possession of this attractive bright yellow metal has been a mark of wealth for thousands of years.
3. Y C M	Because it can easily be formed into complex shapes, this metal is used in the manufacture of a variety of products such as cans, paper clips, safety pins, and utensils.
4. C F E M	One of the cheapest and most useful metals, this metal is the basic material of steel.
5. D T I J	In spite of its usefulness, if too much of this metal builds up in the body, poisoning results. Thus, the U.S. government now restricts the amount of this metal in paint and gasoline, as well as the amount that can be released into the air.
6. W T F A G F Q	Named for the swift messenger of the gods in Roman mythology, this metal is also called quicksilver because, unlike any other metal, it is a liquid at room temperature.
7. O C D B T F	Harder than gold but softer than copper, this metal is used in jewelry and tableware. The largest consumer of this metal is the photographic industry which uses it for such purposes as coating and developing film.
8. A X F E W C G W	Hard, brittle, and gray, this metal is used to plate automobile bumpers, door handles, and trim.
9. W I M K I M T O T	A plentiful element found throughout much of the earth's crust, this metal is used in the manufacture of dry cell batteries and many dyes.
10. A E H I D Y	A rare metal, one of its most widely-known uses is for the treatment of cancer and the diagnosis of certain diseases.

Lesson 14

Antaeus: Part I

Words for Study

Antaeus	initials	domain	enterprises
sedan	resolute	vacant	laborious
parapet	bale	contemplate	toilsome
robust	stolid	distracted	dilated

Antaeus: Part I

by Borden Deal

This was during the wartime, when lots of people were coming North for jobs in factories and war industries, when people moved around a lot more than they do now and sometimes kids were thrown into new groups and new lives that were completely different from anything they had ever known before. I remember this one kid, T.J. his name was, from somewhere down South, whose family moved into our building during that time. They'd come North with everything they owned piled into the back seat of an old-model sedan that you wouldn't expect could make the trip, with T.J. and his three younger sisters riding shakily on top of the load of junk.

Our building was just like all the others there, with families crowded into a few rooms, and I guess there were twenty-five or thirty kids about my age in that one building. Of course, there were a few of us who formed a gang and ran together all the time after school, and I was the one who brought T.J. in and started the whole thing.

The building right next door to us was a factory where they made walking dolls. It was a low building with a flat, tarred roof that had a parapet all around it about head-high and we'd found out a long time before that no one, not even the watchman, paid any attention to the roof because it was higher than any of the other buildings around. So my gang used the roof as a headquarters. We could get up there by crossing over to the fire escape from our own roof on a plank and then going on up. It was a secret place for us, where nobody else could go without our permission.

I remember the day I first took T.J. up there to meet the gang. He was a stocky, robust kid with a shock of white hair, nothing sissy about him except his voice—he talked in this slow, gentle voice like you never heard before. He talked different from any of us and you noticed it right away. But I liked him anyway, so I told him to come on up.

We climbed up over the parapet and dropped down on the roof. The rest of the gang were already there.

"Hi," I said. I jerked my thumb at T.J. "He just moved into the building yesterday."

He just stood there, not scared or anything, just looking, like the first time you see somebody you're not sure you're going to like.

"Hi," Blackie said. "Where are you from?"

"Marion County," T.J. said.

We laughed. "Marion County?" I said. "Where's that?"

He looked at me for a moment like I was a stranger, too. "It's in Alabama," he said, like I ought to know where it was.

"What's your name?" Charley said.

"T.J.," he said, looking back at him. He had pale blue eyes that looked washed-out but he looked directly at Charley, waiting for his reaction. He'll be all right, I thought. No sissy in him—except that voice. Who ever talked like that?

"T.J.," Blackie said. "That's just initials. What's your real name? Nobody in the world has just initials."

"I do," he said. "And they're T.J. That's all the name I got."

His voice was resolute with knowledge of his rightness and for a moment no one had anything to say. T.J. looked around at the rooftop and down at the black tar under his feet. "Down yonder where I come from," he said, "we played out in the woods. Don't you-all have no woods around here?"

"Naw," Blackie said. "There's the park a few blocks over, but it's full of kids and cops and old women. You can't do a thing."

T.J. kept looking at the tar under his feet. "You mean you ain't got no fields to raise nothing in?—no watermelons or nothing?"

"Naw," I said scornfully. "What do you want to grow something for? The folks can buy everything they need at the store."

He looked at me again with that strange, unknowing look. "In Marion County," he said, "I had my own acre of cotton and my own acre of corn. It was mine to plant and make ever' year."

He sounded like it was something to be proud of, and in some obscure way it made the rest of us angry. "Jesus!" Blackie said. "Who'd want to have their own acre of cotton and corn? That's just work. What can you do with an acre of cotton and corn?"

T.J. looked at him. "Well, you get part of the bale offen your acre," he said seriously. "And I fed my acre of corn to my calf."

We didn't really know what he was talking about, so we were more puzzled than angry; otherwise, I guess, we'd have chased him off the roof and wouldn't let him be part of our gang. But he was strange and different and we were all attracted by his stolid sense of rightness and belonging, maybe by the strange softness of his voice contrasting our own tones of speech into harshness.

He moved his foot against the black tar. "We could make our own field right here," he said softly, thoughtfully. "Come spring we could raise us what we want to—watermelons and garden truck and no telling what all."

"You'd have to be a good farmer to make these tar roofs grow any watermelons," I said. We all laughed.

But T.J. looked serious. "We could haul us some dirt up here," he said. "And spread it out even and water it and before you know it we'd have us a crop in here." He looked at us intently. "Wouldn't that be fun?"

"They wouldn't let us," Blackie said quickly.

"I thought you said this was you-all's roof," T.J. said to me. "That you-all could do anything you wanted to up here."

"They've never bothered us," I said. I felt the idea beginning to catch fire in me. It was a big idea and it took a while for it to sink in but the more I thought about it the better I liked it. "Say," I said to the gang. "He might have something there. Just make us a regular roof garden, with flowers and grass and trees and everything. And all ours, too," I said. "We wouldn't let anybody up here except the ones we wanted to."

"It'd take a while to grow trees," T.J. said quickly, but we weren't paying any attention to him. They were all talking about it suddenly, all excited with the idea after I'd put it in a way they could catch hold of it. Only rich people had roof gardens, we knew, and the idea of our own private domain excited them.

"We could bring it up in sacks and boxes," Blackie said. "We'd have to do it while the folks weren't paying any attention to us, for we'd have to come up to the roof of our building and then cross over with it."

"Where could we get the dirt?" somebody said worriedly.

"Out of those vacant lots over close to the school," Blackie said. "Nobody'd notice if we scraped it up."

I slapped T.J. on the shoulder. "Man, you had a wonderful idea," I said, and everybody grinned at him, remembering that he had started it. "Our own private roof garden."

He grinned back. "It'll be ourn," he said. "All ourn." Then he looked thoughtful again. "Maybe I can lay my hands on some cotton seed, too. You think we could raise us some cotton?"

We'd started big projects before at one time or another, like any gang of kids, but they'd always petered out for lack of organization and direction. But this one didn't — somehow or other

T.J. kept it going all through the winter months. He kept talking about the watermelons and the cotton we'd raise, come spring, and when even that wouldn't work he'd switch around to my idea of flowers and grass and trees, though he was always honest enough to add that it'd take a while to get any trees started. He always had it on his mind and he'd mention it in school, getting them lined up to carry dirt that afternoon, saying in a casual way that he reckoned a few more weeks ought to see the job through.

Our little area of private earth grew slowly. T.J. was smart enough to start in one corner of the building, heaping up the carried earth two or three feet thick, so that we had an immediate result to look at, to contemplate with awe. Some of the evenings T.J. alone was carrying earth up to the building, the rest of the gang distracted by other enterprises or interests, but T.J. kept plugging along on his own and eventually we'd all come back to him again and then our own little acre would grow more rapidly.

He was careful about the kind of dirt he'd let us carry up there and more than once he dumped a sandy load over the parapet into the areaway below because it wasn't good enough. He found out the kinds of earth in all the vacant lots for blocks around. He'd pick it up and feel it and smell it, frozen though it was sometimes and then he'd say it was good growing soil or it wasn't worth anything and we'd have to go on somewhere else.

Thinking about it now, I don't see how he kept us at it. It was hard work, lugging paper sacks and boxes of dirt all the way up the stairs of our own buildings, keeping out of the way of the grown-ups so they wouldn't catch on to what we were doing. They probably wouldn't have cared, for they didn't pay much attention to us, but we wanted to keep it secret anyway. Then we had to go through the trap door to our roof, teeter over a plank to the fire escape, then climb two or three stories to the parapet and drop down onto the roof. All that for a small pile of earth that sometimes didn't seem worth the effort.

But T.J. kept the vision bright within us, his words shrewd and calculated toward the fulfillment of his dream; and he worked harder than any of us. He seemed driven toward a goal that we couldn't see, a particular point in time that would be definitely marked by signs and wonders that only he could see.

The laborious earth just lay there during the cold months, inert and lifeless, the clods lumpy and cold under our feet when we walked over it. But one day it rained and afterward there was a softness in the air and the earth was live and giving again with moisture and warmth. That evening T.J. smelled the air, his nostrils dilating with the odor of the earth under his feet.

"It's spring," he said and there was a gladness rising in his voice that filled us all with the same feeling. "It's mighty late for it, but it's spring. I'd just about decided it wasn't never gonna get here at all."

We were all sniffing at the air, too, trying to smell it the way that T.J. did, and I can still remember the sweet odor of the earth under our feet. It was the first time in my life that spring and spring earth had meant anything to me. I looked at T.J. then, knowing in a faint way the hunger within him through the toilsome winter months, knowing the dream that lay behind his plan. He was a new Antaeus, preparing his own bed of strength.

"Planting time," he said. "We'll have to find us some seed."

Continued in the next lesson...

1 **Understanding the Story.** Put the letter of the best answer on the line to the left.

_____ 1. The narrator of "Antaeus" is _____.

(a) a member of the gang
(b) Blackie
(c) T.J.
(d) Charlie

_____ 2. "Antaeus" takes place during _____.

(a) the Gay Nineties
(b) the Roaring Twenties
(c) the Great Depression
(d) World War II

_____ 3. The gang used the doll factory roof for their headquarters because _____.

(a) it was near everyone's home
(b) it was protected by a parapet
(c) the building was deserted
(d) no one bothered them there

_____ 4. Which word *least* describes T.J.?

(a) robust
(b) resolute
(c) sissy
(d) stocky

_____ 5. What does the narrator find most unusual about T.J.?

(a) his background
(b) his cowardice
(c) his voice
(d) his name

_____ 6. What does T.J. find most unusual about his new environment?

(a) the harshness of the people
(b) the lack of open land
(c) the number of policemen
(d) the pace of city life

_____ 7. The gang's initial reaction to T.J.'s description of his crops is _____.

(a) admiration
(b) jealousy
(c) anger
(d) worry

_____ 8. The narrator _____ T.J.'s idea of creating a garden.

(a) disagrees with
(b) rejects
(c) questions
(d) supports

_____ 9. Which of the following indicates that T.J. knows something about farming?

(a) He rejects some of the dirt.
(b) He avoids adults while carrying dirt to the roof.
(c) He successfully organizes the gang to carry dirt to the roof.
(d) He works harder than the other gang members.

_____ 10. *Antaeus* is the name of a figure in Greek mythology. Based on what happens in the first part of the story, which description of Antaeus is correct?

(a) the god of the underworld and dispenser of earthly riches
(b) a giant whose strength was renewed by contact with the earth
(c) a fabled king whose power enabled him to turn everything he touched to gold
(d) a hero noted for his great strength and for having accomplished twelve gigantic tasks imposed upon him

2 **What Do You Think?** Answer the following questions in good sentence form. Use details from the story and personal explanations to support your answers.

1. What qualities does T.J. have that help to make the gang's project a success?

____

____

____

____

____

2. What reasons do you think the boys have for continuing to work on the project?

____

____

____

____

____

3 Word Relationships. On the line to the left, write the letter of the answer that best completes each statement.

_____ 1. Omnivore is to bear as _____.

(a) carnivore is to hippopotamus
(b) parasite is to flea
(c) herbivore is to spider
(d) shark is to scavenger

_____ 2. Switzerland is to Europe as _____.

(a) Berkeley is to the United States
(b) Brazil is to Central America
(c) Egypt is to Africa
(d) Holland is to Scandinavia

_____ 3. Sand is to granular as _____.

(a) lead is to toxic
(b) Gila monster is to mythical
(c) parapet is to obscure
(d) crabgrass is to brackish

_____ 4. Malaria is to malady as _____.

(a) angler is to mariner
(b) boulder is to detritus
(c) mineral is to organism
(d) copper is to metal

_____ 5. Hunter is to game as _____.

(a) lode is to miner
(b) pallbearer is to funeral
(c) predator is to prey
(d) tarantula is to habitat

_____ 6. Laborious is to toilsome as _____.

(a) dilated is to compressed
(b) determined is to resolute
(c) robust is to stolid
(d) toxic is to moribund

_____ 7. Cascade is to waterfall as _____.

(a) canyon is to estuary
(b) glen is to meadow
(c) mountain is to range
(d) ravine is to gorge

_____ 8. Distracted is to attentive as _____.

(a) accessible is to remote
(b) fearsome is to fearless
(c) improbable is to impossible
(d) predatory is to instinctive

_____ 9. Seattle is to Washington as _____.

(a) Carson City is to Montana
(b) New Orleans is to Louisiana
(c) Charleston is to North Carolina
(d) Pittsburgh is to Virginia

_____ 10. Consolation is to comfort as _____.

(a) DDT is to contamination
(b) domain is to terrain
(c) enterprise is to undertaking
(d) pollination is to predation

4 **From the Earth.** To identify the plants that match the following descriptions, choose one word from List A and add a word from List B to it. Refer to a dictionary or other reference for those items which give you difficulty. The first one is done to get you started.

List A		List B	
arrow	✓hem	ease	radish
buck	horse	flower	rod
fox	penny	glove	root
golden	spear	✓lock	royal
hearts	sun	mint	wheat

hemlock 1. T.J. and his friends would not have chosen this poisonous herb for their garden. Unfortunately, this plant strongly resembles parsley, and children have been poisoned when they made whistles or peashooters from its hollow stems.

__________ 2. Grown as a field crop for its seeds, these seeds are then ground into flour, mostly for pancake mixtures.

__________ 3. This mint plant has clusters of small, purplish flowers and yields an oil which is used in perfumes, medicines, candy, and chewing gum.

__________ 4. Only soybeans yield more vegetable oil than this plant which has showy yellow flowers. Its seeds are used in making margarine, cooking oil, and snack foods.

__________ 5. The leaves of this poisonous plant, when dried, are the source of the drug, digitalis—a medicine which is useful for certain heart ailments.

__________ 6. Some Americans have suggested that this plant with its clusters of small yellow flowers should be proclaimed our national flower. Thomas A. Edison devised a method for extracting rubber from this plant, but it proved too costly for commercial use.

__________ 7. The root of this common, tropical plant is used to make a light starch which serves as an ingredient in puddings, pie fillings, and other desserts. American Indians used this root to absorb poison from arrow wounds.

__________ 8. The shredded or grated root of this coarse plant is often preserved in vinegar in order to keep its sharp, biting odor and taste.

__________ 9. This herb of the mint family yields an oil which is used to make various medicines, perfumes, and mosquito repellents.

__________ 10. This lovely pansy has several other romantic names such as "kiss-me-at-the-garden-gate," "love's idleness," and "Johnny-jump-up."

5 **If You Were a Writer...** With the help of the dictionary, decide which figure from Greek mythology listed below could be used in the title of your work.

Aphrodite	Hercules
Apollo	Midas
Ares	Narcissus
Athena	Pandora
Atlas	Zeus

_______________ 1. A biography about the president of an international business whose power is so vast that no one dares to question his decisions.

_______________ 2. A drama about a warrior who desires nothing from life other than the glory and honor offered to him on the battlefield.

_______________ 3. A long essay in which wisdom is presented as the highest virtue worthy of man's striving.

_______________ 4. A magazine article about an incredible weightlifter who is able to triumphantly master any challenge presented to him.

_______________ 5. A mournful poem about a young woman who is so dejected that she passes each day simply staring at her reflection in the mirror on her dressing table.

_______________ 6. A romance about a woman whose beauty is so stunning that when people come into her presence, their thoughts immediately turn to love.

_______________ 7. A sad tale of a man who is so burdened by life's difficulties that he feels as if the weight of the entire world is upon his shoulders.

_______________ 8. A short story about a nosy woman who—although not an evil person by nature—somehow manages to bring strife and confusion into the lives of all who have the misfortune of meeting her.

_______________ 9. A tale of uncontrollable greed in which the main character's thirst for riches almost costs him his very life.

_______________ 10. An adventure about a dazzling young man who brightens people's lives with his beautiful ballads which he sings to the accompaniment of his guitar.

Lesson 15

Antaeus: Part II

Words for Study

hesitant	violation	levied	infinitely
ventilators	principles	sterile	texture
sowing	catalogue	finality	contemplation
bravado	esoteric	frenzied	anonymous

Antaeus: Part II

by Borden Deal

"What do we do?" Blackie said. "How do we do it?"

"First we'll have to break up the clods," T.J. said. "That won't be hard to do. Then we plant the seed and after a while they come up. Then you got you a crop." He frowned. "But you ain't got it raised yet. You got to tend it and hoe it and take care of it and all the time it's growing and growing, while you're awake and while you're asleep. Then you lay it by when it's growed and let it ripen and then you got a crop."

"There's those wholesale seed houses over on Sixth," I said. "We could probably swipe some grass seed over there."

T.J. looked at the earth. "You-all seem mighty set on raising some grass," he said. "I ain't never put no effort into that. I spent all my life trying not to raise grass."

"But it's pretty," Blackie said. "We could play on it and take sun baths. Like having our own lawn. Lots of people got lawns."

"Well," T.J. said. He looked at the rest of us, hesitant for the first time. He kept on looking at us for a moment. "I did have it in mind to raise some corn and vegetables. But we'll plant grass."

He was smart. He knew where to give in. And I don't suppose it made any difference to him, really. He just wanted to grow something, even if it was grass.

"Of course," he said, "I do think we ought to plant a row of watermelons. They'd be mighty nice to eat while we was a-laying on that grass."

We all laughed. "All right," I said. "We'll plant us a row of watermelons."

Things went very quickly then. Perhaps half the roof was covered with the earth, the half that wasn't broken by ventilators, and we swiped pocketfuls of grass seed from the open bins in the wholesale seed house, mingling among the buyers on Saturdays and during the school lunch hour. T.J. showed us how to prepare the earth, breaking up the clods and smoothing it and sowing the grass seed. It looked rich and black now with moisture, receiving of the seed, and it seemed that the grass sprang up overnight, pale green in the early spring.

We couldn't keep from looking at it, unable to believe that we had created this delicate growth. We looked at T.J. with understanding now, knowing the fulfillment of the plan he had carried alone within his mind. We had worked without full understanding of the task but he had known all the time.

We found that we couldn't walk or play on the delicate blades, as we had expected to, but we didn't mind. It was enough just to look at it, to realize that it was the work of our own hands, and each evening the whole gang was there, trying to measure the growth that had been achieved that day.

One time a foot was placed on the plot of ground— one time only, Blackie stepping onto it with sudden bravado. Then he looked at the crushed blades and there was shame in his face. He did not do it again. This was his grass, too, and not to be desecrated. No one said anything, for it was not necessary.

T.J. had reserved a small section for watermelons and he was still trying to find some seed for it. The wholesale house didn't have any watermelon seed and we didn't know where we could lay our hands on them. T.J. shaped the earth into mounds, ready to receive them, three mounds lying in a straight line along the edge of the grass plot.

We had just about decided that we'd have to buy the seed if we were to get them. It was a violation of our principles, but we were anxious to get the watermelons started. Somewhere or other, T.J. got his hands on a seed catalogue and brought it one evening to our roof garden.

"We can order them now," he said, showing us the catalogue. "Look!"

We all crowded around, looking at the fat, green watermelons pictured in full color on the pages. Some of them were split open, showing the red, tempting meat, making our mouths water.

"Now we got to scrape up some seed money," T.J. said, looking at us. "I got a quarter. How much you-all got?"

We made up a couple of dollars between us and T.J. nodded his head. "That'll be more than enough. Now we got to decide what kind to get. I think them Kleckley Sweets. What do you-all think?"

He was going into esoteric matters beyond our reach. We hadn't even known there were different kinds of melons. So we just nodded our heads and agreed that Yes, we thought the Kleckley Sweets, too.

"I'll order them tonight," T.J. said. "We ought to have them in a few days."

"*What are you boys doing up here*?" an adult voice said behind us.

It startled us, for no one had ever come up here before, in all the time we had been using the roof of the factory. We jerked around and saw three men standing near the trap door at the other end of the roof. They weren't policemen, or night watchmen, but three men in plump business suits, looking at us. They walked toward us.

"What are you boys doing up here?" the one in the middle said again.

We stood still, guilt heavy among us, levied by the tone of voice, and looked at the three strangers.

The men stared at the grass flourishing behind us. "*What's this?*" the man said. "*How did this get up here*?"

"Sure is growing good, ain't it?" T.J. said conversationally. "We planted it."

The men kept looking at the grass as if they didn't believe it. It was a thick carpet over the earth now, a patch of deep greenness startling in the sterile industrial surroundings.

"Yes sir," T.J. said proudly. "We toted the earth up here and planted that grass." He fluttered the seed catalogue. "And we're fixing to plant us some watermelon."

The man looked at him then, his eyes strange and faraway. "What do you mean, putting this on the roof of my building?" he said. "*Do you want to go to jail?*"

T.J. looked shaken. The rest of us were silent, frightened by the authority of his voice. We had grown up aware of adult authority, of policemen and night watchmen and teachers, and this man sounded like all the others. But it was a new thing to T.J.

"Well, you wan't using the roof," T.J. said. He paused a moment and added shrewdly, "So we just thought to pretty it up a little bit."

"And sag it so I'd have to rebuild it," the man said sharply. He started turning away, saying to another man behind him, "See that all that junk is shoveled off by tomorrow."

"Yes sir," the man said.

T.J. started forward. "*You can't do that,*" he said. "*We toted it up here and it's our earth. We planted it and raised it and toted it up here.*"

The man stared at him coldly. "But it's my building," he said. "It's to be shoveled off tomorrow."

"*It's our earth,*" T.J. said desperately. "*You ain't got no right*!"

The men walked on without listening and descended clumsily through the trap door. T.J. stood looking after them, his body tense with anger, until they had disappeared. They wouldn't even argue with him, wouldn't let him defend his earth-rights.

He turned to us. "We won't let 'em do it," he said fiercely. "We'll stay up here all day tomorrow and the day after that and we won't let 'em do it."

We just looked at him. We knew that there was no stopping it. He saw it in our faces, and his face wavered for a moment before he gripped it into determination.

"They ain't got no right," he said. "It's our earth. It's our land. Can't nobody touch a man's own land."

We kept on looking at him, listening to the words but knowing that it was no use. The adult world had descended on us even in our richest dream and we knew there was no calculating the adult world, no fighting it, no winning against it.

We started moving slowly toward the parapet and the fire escape, avoiding a last look at the green beauty of the earth that T.J. had planted for us—had planted deeply in our minds as well as in our experience. We filed slowly over the edge and down the steps to the plank, T.J. coming last, and all of us could feel the weight of his grief behind us.

"*Wait a minute,*" he said suddenly, his voice harsh with the effort of calling. We stopped and turned, held by the tone of his voice, and looked up at him standing above us on the fire escape.

"We can't stop them?" he said, looking down at us, his face strange in the dusky light. "There ain't no way to stop 'em?"

"No," said Blackie with finality. "They own the building."

We stood still for a moment, looking up at T.J., caught into inaction by the decision working in his face. He stared back at us and his face was pale and mean in the poor light, with a bald nakedness in his skin like cripples have sometimes.

"*They ain't gonna touch my earth,*" he said fiercely. "*They ain't gonna lay a hand on it! Come on!*"

He turned around and started up the fire escape again, almost running against the effort of climbing. We followed more slowly, not knowing what he intended. By the time we reached him, he had seized a board and thrust it into the soil, scooping it up and flinging it over the parapet into the area below. He straightened and looked at us.

"*They can't touch it,*" he said. "*I won't let 'em lay a dirty hand on it!*"

We saw it then. He stooped to his labor again and we followed, the gusts of his anger moving in frenzied labor among us as we scattered along the edge of the earth, scooping it and throwing it over the parapet destroying with anger the growth we had nurtured with such tender care. The soil carried so laboriously upward to the light and the sun cascaded swiftly into the dark areaway, the green blades of grass crumpled and twisted in the falling.

It took less time than you would think—the task of destruction is infinitely easier than that of creation. We stopped at the end leaving only a scattering of loose soil, and when it was finally over a stillness stood among the group and over the factory buildings. We looked down at the bare sterility of black tar, felt the harsh texture of it under the soles of our shoes, and the anger had gone out of us, leaving only a sore aching in our minds like overstretched muscles.

T.J. stood for a moment, his breathing slowing from anger and effort, caught into the same contemplation of destruction as all of us. He stooped slowly, finally, and picked up a lonely blade of grass left trampled under our feet and put it between his teeth, tasting it, sucking the greenness out of it into his mouth. Then he started walking toward the fire escape, moving before any of us were ready to move, and disappeared over the edge.

We followed him but he was already halfway down to the ground, going on past the board where we crossed over, climbing down into the areaway. We saw the last section swing down with his weight and then he stood on the concrete below us, looking at the small pile of anonymous earth scattered by our throwing. Then he walked across the place where we could see him and disappeared toward the street without glancing back, without looking up to see us watching him.

They did not find him for two weeks. Then the Nashville police caught him just outside the Nashville freight yards. He was walking along the railroad tracks; still heading south, still heading home.

As for us, who had no remembered home to call us—none of us ever again climbed the escape-way to the roof.

1 **Understanding the Story.** Answer the following questions in good sentence form.

1. What does the gang want to plant in their roof garden? How does T.J. respond to this?

2. What does Blackie do with "sudden bravado"? How do the other members of the gang respond to this?

3. What are the boys doing just before they are confronted by the owner of the building?

4. Describe the mood of the owner. Explain the reason for his mood.

5. In what way is T.J.'s response to the owner's demands different from that of the other boys?

6. What actions are taken to follow up T.J.'s claim: "They ain't gonna touch my earth"?

2 **What Do You Think?** Answer the following questions in good sentence form. Be sure to include reasons to support your answers.

1. If you had been the owner of the building, how would you have approached the boys about their grass garden?

2. Why does T.J. run away? Do you think he will eventually settle into the routines of city life, or will he probably run away again?

3 **Which Word Does Not Fit?** Choose the word in each row which does *not* fit and write it on the line.

1. Atlas	Jupiter	Mars	Mercury	Neptune	________
2. stamp	stomp	trample	traverse	tread	________
3. Cherokee	Choctaw	Polynesian	Seminole	Sioux	________
4. dedication	energy	muscle	strength	vigor	________
5. abstain	confine	limit	restrain	restrict	________
6. gap	gorge	gully	ravine	switchback	________
7. doubtful	hesitant	humble	skeptical	wavering	________
8. chromium	cobalt	laurel	manganese	mercury	________
9. crinkle	crumple	rumple	wriggle	wrinkle	________
10. lurch	stagger	stumble	teeter	waddle	________
11. bale	chunk	clod	hunk	lump	________
12. Adams	McKinley	Monroe	Nobel	Taft	________
13. confer	contemplate	ponder	reflect	study	________
14. blemish	deface	disfigure	mutilate	wither	________
15. cloak	disguise	forebode	shield	shroud	________

4 **Homonym Review.** For each set, identify the homonyms which match the definitions. The first one is done to get you started.

doe ________ 1. A female deer, hare, or kangaroo

dough ________ A mixture of liquid, flour, and other dry ingredients

________ 2. The capital of Italy

________ To wander about aimlessly

________ 3. Any creature hunted or caught for food; a victim

________ To make an earnest request to God

________ 4. A hole or tunnel dug in the ground by a small animal

________ A small donkey, especially one used as a pack animal

________ 5. An elected or appointed group who advises or governs

________ To recommend, advise, or offer guidance

________ 6. A passage between a row of seats as in an auditorium

________ A small island

________ 7. A heavy burden; a supported weight or mass

________ A vein of mineral ore; a rich source or supply

________ 8. To make, repair, or fasten with a needle and thread

________ To scatter seed over the ground for growing

________ 9. A basic truth; a rule or standard of good behavior

________ The head of an elementary school or high school

________ 10. A large bound package of raw or finished materials

________ Money exchanged for the release of an arrested person; to empty water out of a boat by scooping or dipping

5 **A Logic Problem.** Four other children were more successful in growing a roof garden than were T.J. and his friends. Each of the four children planted a different vegetable. From the four clues, find the full name of each child and the vegetable he or she planted.

Clue 1: Neither the North child nor the Lane child planted cauliflower.

Clue 2: Bess did not plant cauliflower and her last name is neither North nor Lane.

Clue 3: One child planted artichokes and another child's last name is Jones. The other two children are Alan and Bess. (Note that all four children are mentioned in this clue.)

Clue 4: Neither Lucy nor the Kelly child nor the North child planted asparagus.

Use the chart on this page to solve this logic problem. Enter all information obtained from the clues, using an **N** to indicate a definite *no* and a **Y** to show a definite *yes*. The information from Clue 1 has been entered to get you started. Remember: Once you enter a definite *yes* (Y), you can place a *no* (N) in the other three boxes in both that row and that column in that section of the chart. You will probably have to read the clues several times to complete the puzzle. Fill in the sentences at the bottom as you figure out the answers.

	Jones	Kelly	Lane	North	artichokes	asparagus	broccoli	cauliflower
Alan								
Bess								
Dennis								
Lucy								
artichokes								
asparagus								
broccoli								
cauliflower			N	N				

__________ Jones planted ________________.

__________ Kelly planted ________________.

__________ Lane planted ________________.

__________ North planted ________________.

Review: Lessons 1-15

1 **Definitions.** Match the words listed below with the correct definitions.

anonymous	diagnosis	migrant	substantial
bravado	emphatic	resolve	terrain
cache	levy	sediment	vegetation
capability	malady	specter	vigor

________________ 1. a disease, sickness, or illness

________________ 2. a ghost; a mental image; a foreboding

________________ 3. a region; a particular geographical area; ground

________________ 4. active physical or mental strength; healthy energy

________________ 5. false bravery; a swaggering show of courage

________________ 6. having an unknown or withheld name

________________ 7. solidly built; ample; actual; real

________________ 8. bold and definite in expression or action

________________ 9. the plants of an area or region

________________ 10. to impose and collect (a tax, for example)

________________ 11. material that settles to the bottom of a liquid

________________ 12. a determination or decision; fixed purpose; to make a firm decision about

________________ 13. ability; the capacity to be used, treated, or developed for a specific purpose

________________ 14. a person, animal, bird, or fish that moves from one region to another by chance, instinct, or plan

________________ 15. the process of recognizing a disease by its symptoms; a conclusion based on analysis

________________ 16. a hole or similar hiding place for concealing or storing something

2 **Using Context Clues: Part 1.** Use the context clues to determine which pair of words best completes each sentence. Write the pair in the blanks.

1. The ____________ carved his initials on a nearby ____________ to mark the site of his triumphant catch.
   (a) angler — alder (c) Marine — laurel
   (b) infielder — foxglove (d) predator — hemlock

2. David Brower, founder of Friends of Earth, ____________ reminds his audiences that the ____________ of our environment cannot continue.
   (a) astonishingly — contamination (c) laboriously — sterility
   (b) consistently — desecration (d) modestly — radiation

3. The conversation in the check-out line became ____________ as the shoppers bemoaned how prices had ____________ in just the past few months.
   (a) distracted — cascaded (c) spirited — skyrocketed
   (b) esoteric — teetered (d) frenzied — dilated

4. Huddled behind the ____________, the combatant's former bravado gave way to outright cowardice as he ____________ his fate.
   (a) crater — abandoned (c) parapet — pondered
   (b) delta — diagnosed (d) ravine — resolved

5. When asked how she happened to know so much about the gold market, Molly replied casually, "Oh, I like to ____________ in ____________."
   (a) contemplate — luxury (c) excel — jewelry
   (b) dabble — economics (d) venture — mineralogy

6. The ambassador was ____________ because of his ____________ remark about his host country.
   (a) exploited — emphatic (c) recommended — turbulent
   (b) trampled — ruthless (d) recalled — insulting

7. "Your ____________ to this company has ____________ improved our chances of beating the competition," beamed the supervisor as he proudly awarded the silver plaque to Hernando.
   (a) consistency — intently (c) dedication — inevitably
   (b) contribution — infinitely (d) self-mastery — independently

8. ______________ by cycles of chills, fever, and sweating, malaria is ______________ by the bite of an infected female mosquito.

(a) Characterized — transmitted
(b) Classified — transfixed
(c) Complicated — transformed
(d) Contaminated — transacted

9. That she had tried to follow her ______________ was Diana's only consolation as she bid farewell to the members of the town ______________ for the last time.

(a) principals — council
(b) principals — counsel
(c) principles — council
(d) principles — counsel

3 **Using Context Clues: Part 2.** As we know, a word can have more than one meaning. All the definitions for each underlined word are correct, but only one matches the word as it is used in the sentence. Write the letter of the correct definition on the line.

______ 1. Anxious about her brother who sulked in front of the TV set night after night, Rachel finally said, "Are you going to vegetate in that armchair for the rest of your life just because your girlfriend jilted you?"

(a) to produce vegetation
(b) to grow or sprout as a plant does
(c) to lead a humdrum existence without exertion of body or mind

______ 2. "If you want to know how to enjoy your life more," advised the counselor gently, "you've got to examine your interior life more closely rather than putting all the blame on outer circumstances."

(a) of or relating to one's mental or spiritual being
(b) situated away from a coast or border
(c) the inner portion or area of something

______ 3. When none of the distractions she offered the screaming baby calmed him down, the frantic baby-sitter decided she had better call the parents immediately.

(a) anything that draws attention away, especially an amusement
(b) extreme mental or emotional disturbance
(c) the act of being pulled in conflicting directions

______ 4. Upon being asked by the reporter if working the soil gave him a sense of belonging to the land, the farmer replied gruffly, "Son, today farming's nothing but another enterprise."

(a) energy or spirit for starting a new or difficult undertaking
(b) a business or undertaking, especially one of some risk
(c) boldness

______ 5. Ernst was looking forward to the concert tonight when he could just abandon himself to the music and forget about the problems at work.

(a) to desert
(b) to surrender one's claim or right to
(c) to yield oneself completely, as to an emotion

______ 6. In Mrs. Kennecott's capacity as hostess, she tried to make sure that none of the guests at her Christmas party felt left out.

(a) the position in which one functions
(b) the maximum amount that can be contained
(c) the ability to receive, hold, or absorb

______ 7. Having dozed off for a few moments in the niche, the bandit awoke with a start as he heard the sound of approaching horses in the canyon.

(a) a recess in a wall for holding a statue or other ornament
(b) an area within a habitat occupied by an organism
(c) any steep, shallow recess, as in a rock or hill

4 **Putting Sentences in Order.** Below are observations about the earth made by three ecologists. Number the sentences so that they appear in the correct order.

1. ____ We have reached a total of five billion people, and we are plainly failing to feed, house, educate, and employ many of these in basically acceptable fashion.

   ____ Today, the rise of human numbers casts a shadow over planet Earth.

   ____ Worse, the human community is projected to reach at least 10 billion before the population explosion comes to an end early in the 22nd century.

2. ____ This curious mixture is derived from rock which has been weathered by rainwater, gases, ice, and roots, and has slowly broken down into a form which can support many life-forms.

   ____ The next time you tread on earth (as opposed to concrete or asphalt), take a look at what lies at your feet.

   ____ These, in turn, enable it to support plants.

   ____ It is likely to be a fairly loose material, half made up of masses of tiny particles, the other half of water and air.

3. ____ The problem is that the Earth is less than fair in distributing its land resources.

   ____ As a result, some sections have much more fertile soil than others, and some respond much better to constructive human manipulation.

   ____ There is no doubt that we produce enough food to send everybody to bed with a full stomach.

   ____ Yet tens of millions starve, and millions more are malnourished.

---

5 **A Poet's Point of View.** Read the poem below and then answer the questions which follow.

The Forecast
by Dan Jaffe

Perhaps our age has driven us indoors.
We sprawl in the semi-darkness, dreaming sometimes
Of a vague world spinning in the wind.
But we have snapped our locks, pulled down our shades,
Taken all precautions. We shall not be disturbed.
If the earth shakes, it will be on a screen;
And if the prairie wind spills down our streets
And covers us with leaves, the weatherman will tell us.

1. According to the poet, what kind of relationship do most of us have with nature?

____

____

____

____

____

2. What "forecast" does the poet seem to be making about mankind's relationship with the earth?

____

____

____

____

____

____

---

3. In a paragraph or poem offer your own forecast about mankind's relationship with the earth.

Unit 4

Change

Change—especially for us living in the twentieth century—is one thing of which we can be certain. It is everywhere. We change; our friends change; inventions and events change the world we live in. Sometimes we welcome these changes and sometimes we don't. In this last unit, you will have the opportunity to explore five writers' thoughts on various aspects of the concept of *change*.

In the reading for Lesson 16, entitled "Life without Furnace, Pipe, or Wire," the author presents a glimpse of what our everyday lives might be like if certain changes had *not* taken place.

In Lesson 17, an excerpt from Anton Chekhov's one-act play "A Marriage Proposal" portrays a change that has always been of interest to writers—a change of heart.

Many people today are not totally happy with the way their lives are going. In the reading for Lesson 18, the American writer Leo Buscaglia suggests that by changing our attitudes we can change our lives for the better.

In the autobiographical excerpt in Lesson 19, the Hall of Fame baseball player Roy Campanella describes the changes that occurred in his life as a result of his world being turned upside down one winter day.

Finally, in "Heir to Tradition," the reading for Lesson 20, the author explores the importance of tradition in our rapidly changing world.

Life without Furnace, Pipe, or Wire

Words for Study

Heraclitus	blatant	ascended	elegant
suspicion	hearth	domestic	intervals
figment	thermostats	hazards	tendency
arduous	chamber	canopy	prestige

Life without Furnace, Pipe, or Wire

Centuries before the birth of Christ, the Greek philosopher Heraclitus wrote, "Nothing endures but change."

Quite often people's first reaction to change is one of doubt, suspicion, or even fear. Perhaps one way to approach change in a more positive light is to imagine what our daily lives would be like if certain changes had never taken place.

One instrument of change with which we are familiar is the invention. In this reading, an American historian presents a picture of life in a typical American home of the nineteenth century where many of the comforts we take so much for granted were no more than a figment of some inventor's imagination.

* * *

No matter how widely they varied, all homes in the early nineteenth century had one big thing in common: none of them could boast a furnace, a pipe, or a wire. Simple life functions, such as keeping warm, taking a bath, or getting set for the night, were pretty much the same in every kind of house. Life was everywhere arduous. In every process, in each piece of equipment, there was a blatant need for improvement.

The open fireplace was still the main source of heat. And it was an exasperating kind of heat. Standing in front of the fire on a cold January night, the householder broiled in front and froze behind. Turning around, he quickly froze in the face and became uncomfortably hot in the seat. Walking fifteen feet to the washstand, he might find the water frozen in the china pitcher.

In every room the furnishings reflected this heating problem. A favorite parlor chair, for example, was the wing chair, with its high back and sides, or "wings." Sitting in it, the householder was exposed only in the front, and, of course, he usually chose to face the fire. Another common object was the foot warmer, a small iron box with a lid and handles. The householder would fill it with glowing coals from the fireplace and carry it elsewhere to use as a hot footstool.

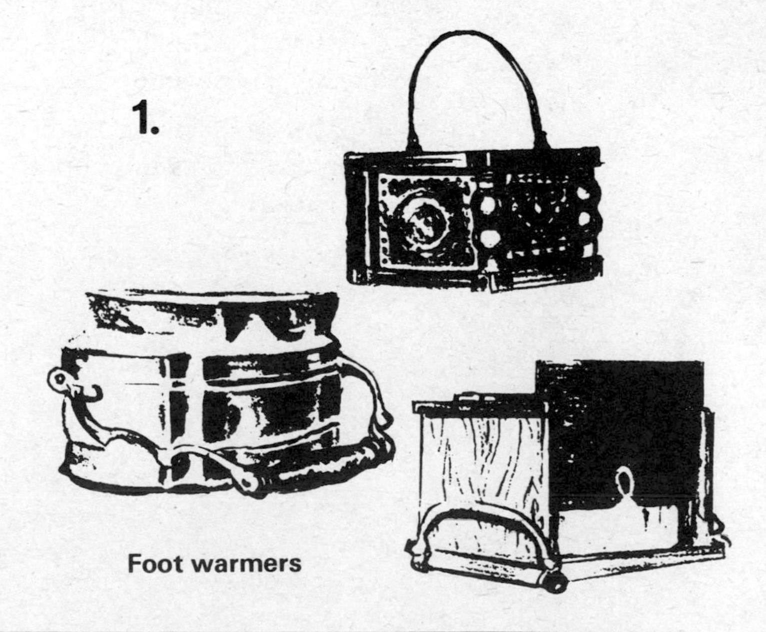

1.

Foot warmers

The men and boys in the house had the enormous and never-ending task of sawing and splitting wood, building and tending fires, lugging out the ashes. Summer was the best time for getting ahead on the winter fuel supply, but even then the kitchen fire had to be kept ablaze.

To start a fire, the householder filled a tinderbox with dry, crumbling wood. With a small steel bar, he would strike a piece of flint stone until sparks fell into the tinder. Then, blowing vigorously, he hoped that the tinder would begin to smolder. Not much better than the caveman's rubbing of sticks, this nineteenth-century process could actually take, even on a dry day, fifteen minutes to produce a fire.

An improved tinderbox, which worked much like a modern cigarette lighter, made the operation somewhat faster and easier to control. It had a steel sparking wheel at one end that would strike the flint several times whenever it was turned. But building up a big hearth fire from a chance spark was still such hard work that the householder seldom risked letting the fire go out.

The first "striking match" was not invented until 1836. Alonzo Phillips, its inventor, would make a wagonload of his phosphorous matches in his factory in Springfield, Massachusetts, and then ride around selling them from door to door. Needless to say, flint and steel were still widely used well into the 1840s.

Not until the 1870s could a person expect his home to be kept reasonably warm by a furnace of some kind. Even then, in the chill early morning, he had to go down cellar, shake down the ashes, poke the clinkers from the grates, pour fresh coal on the fire, and open the draft. For this was still the age of hand-shoveled coal. There would be no thermostats, oil burners, gas furnaces, or electric panels for another half century.

2.

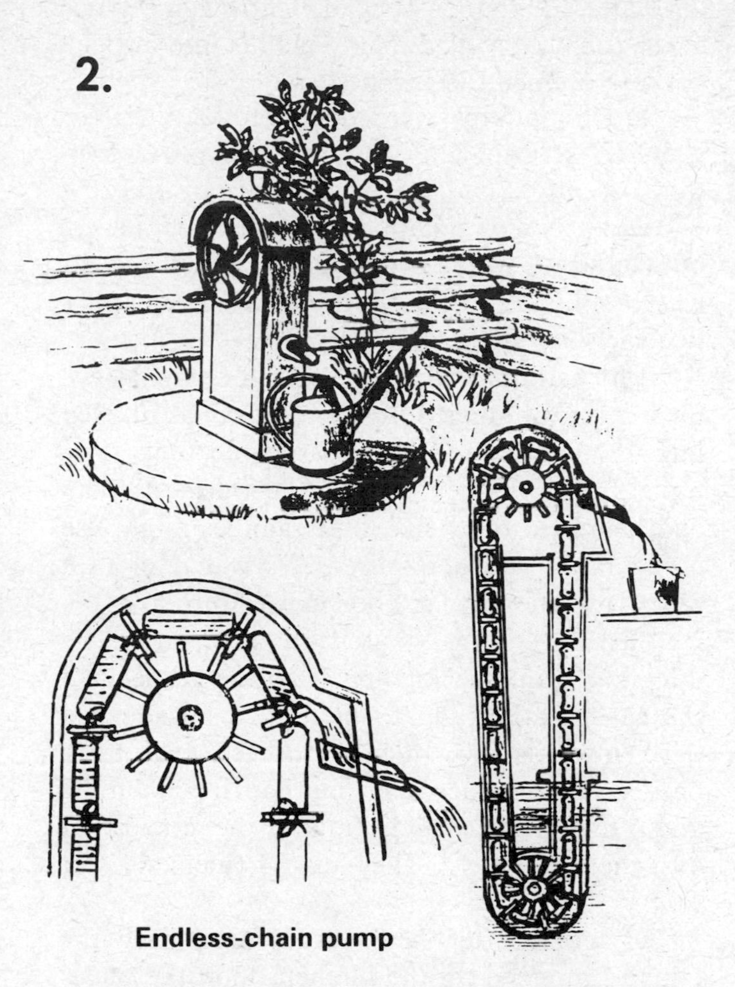

Endless-chain pump

With no plumbing, of course, there were no toilets and lavatories, in the modern sense of the words. Most of the time people used the outhouse, a sheltered seat built over an open pit. When the pit was filled, the males in the family would drag the outhouse to another spot over a new hole and cover up the old one. On a cold night, the ladies and children usually preferred to use a chamber pot, kept under the bed.

The average home had no special room for bathing. A bath, as a matter of fact, was so much trouble that during the work week most people just washed the parts of the body that showed, hoping for a full bath on Saturday night—if not this one, then surely the next.

The first step, and often the hardest, was to get a large enough supply of water to fill a tub. Even in the city, the typical house had its own dug well, surrounded by a latticed well house. One oaken bucket hung at either end of a rope, which ran over a pulley suspended from the ridge-pole of the well-house roof. As he pulled up one bucket full of water, the householder was letting the other, empty one down. Or he might own a chain pump, which carried many small cups fastened along an endless chain. As he turned a crank handle, cups descended upside-down into the water, filled up, ascended right side up, tilted at the top, and spilled their contents into a spout as they resumed their endless journey.

Suction pumps were not manufactured for general use until later in the century. Yet even this invention had its drawbacks. In freezing weather a suction pump always had to be thawed out before it would work at all, and the well-water still had to be carried indoors, a bucket or two each trip.

If he had domestic help, a person might have his big tin tub lugged up from the cellar or shed into his bedroom. But most people took their baths in the kitchen, always the warmest room and nearer to the well. Some families might use a sitz bath, which required less water, or in a pinch, just the regular wooden washtub.

Bathwater was heated in an iron kettle dangling from the kitchen fireplace crane, and the eager bather had to pour it, a bucket at a time, into his tub. In many homes, everybody bathed in the same water, mother first, then the girls, then father, and, finally, the dirtiest of all—the little boys. They used homemade soft soap.

Of course, after the Saturday-night bath, the females mopped up the kitchen floor, the males emptied the tub, a bucket at a time, out the kitchen door, and returned the tub to its storage place.

Nobody knows who deserves the credit for first piping water inside a house in the United States. What is known is that by the middle of the nineteenth century, health hazards forced cities to provide centralized water supplies and sewers.

Even getting ready for bed was hard work in "the good old days." The family retired early for four very good reasons. Illumination was poor because the crude oil lamps and the open fire did not provide much light, and candles were too expensive to be used very extensively on ordinary nights; everybody had to begin work at sunup; bed was the best place to keep warm; and getting there took so long that it was best to begin early.

First there was the serious problem of making sure there would be a fire in the morning. The householder added a "night log" to every fireplace and let it get a good start. In the meantime, he put some live coals and wood chips into a curfew—a small iron pan with a long handle and a cone-shaped tin cover—and set it inside the fireplace. Thus he had a small reserve fire in case the big open fire went out. Then he put more live coals into a long-handled brass pan called a bed warmer. And he banked the big fire with ashes, hoping it would last out the night.

The lady of the house, who had probably been filling the water pitcher on each washstand, now took the bed warmer, slid it slowly up and down between the sheets of each bed, and returned the pan to the hearth. In the late fall in many houses the sheets were replaced by cotton blankets as being less icy to the touch. Older children who could be entrusted with such dangerous tasks might help with the bed warming and the night logs.

About to retire, they put their outer garments away, not in a closet—there were no closets—but in a wardrobe, clothes press, or cupboard. They re-dressed in nightshirts, nightcaps, even night socks.

If people could afford it, they preferred to sleep in what was called a tester bed, with four high posts, a canopy across the top, and curtains that could be closed all around. This was no coil-spring bedstead. That would come later, inspired by the spring seats which carriage builders used in the more elegant buggies.

Rather, it was a cord-type bedstead. Holes were bored at eight-inch intervals through the foot, head, and side rails; sturdy rope was laced through these holes to make a web. A mattress stuffed with hay, straw, or maybe even corn shucks was placed on top of this crisscross rope.

When new, the cord bed was fairly comfortable, but the rope had a distressing tendency to sag with age, forming a kind of hammock, which made things increasingly difficult for occupants of a double bed.

Typical of hundreds of inventions aimed at making life less arduous was the bedstead-cord pin-with-a-crank, patented by John Beyer of Hainsville, Missouri, in 1859. With this gadget the householder could tune up his cord bed, much as he tuned up a banjo, until alas, the cords broke altogether.

Notice that hired help was almost a necessity for the nineteenth century homeowner. A large establishment with several teams of horses and vehicles required a coachman and often a groom, who lived in their own quarters over the coach house. Many families would keep a cow and a few chickens, and maybe hire a farm hand to help with a kitchen garden or an orchard of apple, peach, cherry, and pear trees.

When immigrants were arriving in large numbers, domestic live-in jobs attracted many of them. But with the spread of the factory system, young girls preferred to work in the mills; mill work paid better, allowed more personal freedom, and gave one higher social prestige. With the opening of new territories, domestic work in the East seemed even less attractive as lower-class families sought their own property and fortune in the West. Household servants became harder to find.

Even families not accustomed to having help looked forward to freedom from mere existence chores. In an "open society," in which anyone with ability could improve himself and enjoy life, everybody wanted time to learn, read, plan, relax.

The result was a continuous quest for labor-saving devices. Fortunately, the Industrial Revolution, which had introduced machine methods of production and made money available for research and inventions, could now help to improve home technology.

1 **Understanding the Reading.** An *outline* is a way to organize what we have read so that we can recall information more rapidly. Use the items listed below to complete this outline for information presented in "Life without Furnace, Pipe, or Wire." Note that in outlining, the first word of each item is capitalized.

Baths	Fuel supply	Night log	Tinderbox
Bed warmer	Coal furnace	Open fireplace	Water
Curfew	Kitchen	Outhouse	Water pitcher

Difficulties of Living in the 19th Century

I. Heating Problems

A. ________________ —failed to heat rooms evenly

B. ________________ —needed constant replenishing

C. ________________ —an ineffective piece of equipment which required patience and luck to start a fire

D. ________________ —an improvement over the fireplace as a source of heat but still required daily attention

II. Inconveniences resulting from lack of indoor plumbing

A. ________________ —typical toilet facility before indoor plumbing

B. ________________ —such a nuisance that they were taken only on Saturday

1. ________________ —had to be carted from wells and heated

2. ________________ —used because, even though it didn't offer much privacy, it was the warmest room in the house

III. The routine followed in getting set for the night

A. ________________ —needed to be started in every fireplace

B. ________________ —had to be prepared in case the big open fire went out

C. ________________ —had to be filled on each washstand

D. ________________ —had to be filled and taken to each bed to warm it

2 **What Do You Think?** Answer these questions in good sentence form. Be sure to include well-developed reasons to support your point of view.

1. Of all the inventions you can recall, which invention do you think has contributed most to improving the quality of life?

____

____

____

____

____

____

____

2. Which invention do you think has contributed the least to improving the quality of life?

____

____

____

____

____

____

____

3 **Using Context Clues.** Use the words listed at the left to complete each of these famous quotations about change.

all
endures
nothing

1. "____________ is flux, ____________ stands still. Nothing ____________ but change." (Heraclitus, Greek philosopher, 6th-5th century B.C.)

nature
silly
trial

2. "Human ____________ will not change. In any future great national ____________, compared with the men of this, we shall have as weak and as strong, as ____________ and as wise, as bad and as good." (Abraham Lincoln, 16th U.S. president, 1809-1865)

actually
believe
consist
constantly

3. "Nothing changes more ____________ than the past; for the past that influences our lives does not ____________ of what ____________ happened, but of what men ____________ happened." (Gerald White Johnson, American writer, 1890-1980)

fact
human
pace

4. "The basic ____________ of today is the tremendous ____________ of change in ____________ life." (Jawaharlal Nehru, Indian statesman, 1889-1964)

caused
institutions
organized
wars

5. "____________ are not 'acts of God.' They are ____________ by man, by man-made ____________, by the way in which man has ____________ his society. What man has made, man can change." (Fred M. Vinson, American jurist, 1890-1953)

matters
refrain
reverse
years

6. "You are young, my son, and as the ____________ go by, time will change and even ____________ many of your present opinions. ____________ therefore awhile from setting yourself up as a judge of the highest ____________." (Plato, Greek philosopher, 427?-347 B.C.)

change
favor
life
truths

7. "Most of the ______________ we think we see in ______________ is due to ______________ being in and out of ______________." (Robert Frost, American poet, 1874-1963)

change
remain
same

8. "The more things ______________, the more they ______________ the ______________." (Alphonse Karr, French journalist and writer, 1808-1890)

4 **Writing about Change.** Select one of the quotations from Exercise 3 and copy it on the lines below. Then, in a well-developed paragraph, write your thoughts about this quotation.

Quote: ____

____

____

____

____

____

____

____

____

____

____

5 **Inventors and Their Inventions.** Use a dictionary or encyclopedia as necessary to complete these sentences about American inventors. The first one is done to get you started.

Alexander Graham Bell	George Eastman	Cyrus McCormick
William Burroughs	Thomas Edison	Samuel F. B. Morse
George W. Carver	Robert Fulton	Ransom E. Olds
Samuel Colt	Charles Goodyear	George Westinghouse
Lee DeForest	Elias Howe	Eli Whitney

1. Inventor and civil engineer, ______________________ designed and built the *Clermont*, the first practical and financially successful steamboat, which ushered in a new age in the history of transportation in the early 1800s.

2. ______________________ enjoys two claims to fame. His cotton gin, invented in 1793, helped to make the United States the largest cotton producer in the world; and his method of manufacturing guns by machinery made him the father of mass production in the United States.

3. After many years of struggle, ______________________ received the necessary funds to string a telegraph line from the Capitol Building in Washington, D.C., to Baltimore, Maryland, in 1844. His famous message, "What hath God wrought," proved to be the beginning of many successive years of wealth and fame.

4. While in prison for his debts, ______________________ made his first efforts to change natural rubber into a useful product. Plagued by poor health and financial problems, his eventual perfection of this process brought him little in the way of worldly gain.

5. ______________________ is a good example of the good fortune that can come from being in the right place at the right time. Although not a brilliant or original device, his reaping machine came at a time when the rich, prairie wheatlands were ready for development, and the inventor became a millionaire before he had reached forty.

6. ______________________ developed the first successful repeating pistol, which was patented in England in 1835. After his death, the company he had founded manufactured the famous six-shooters that were used throughout the West.

7. ______________________, having heard that whoever produced a workable sewing machine would make a fortune, patented one in 1846. After an arduous battle to protect his patent, this inventor finally saw the prediction come true.

8. ______________________, the organizer of more than 50 companies and president of 30 corporations, still managed to find time to invent new products. Among the inventions patented by this remarkably energetic man were the air brake for trains, the gas meter, and a system of pipes for safely conducting natural gas into homes.

9. ______________________ once remarked to his family that he would rather be remembered as a teacher of the deaf than as the inventor of the telephone, which he patented in 1876 at the age of 29.

10. ______________________, "the wizard of Menlo Park," stated that the phonograph, which he invented in 1878, was his favorite invention, even though the electric light is usually cited as his greatest invention.

11. ______________________, having invented a machine for coating glass plates in cameras, perfected flexible roll films and produced a light camera which sold for $1 in 1900, enabling millions to enjoy photography as a pastime.

12. His work as a bank clerk made ______________________ recognize the importance of labor-saving devices in accounting; in 1888, he patented an adding machine that was far more reliable than earlier models.

13. Among his many distinctions, ______________________ gained international fame for his research with agricultural products. He successfully developed more than 300 products from peanuts, including a milk substitute, soap, printer's ink, and face powder.

14. A pioneer automobile inventor and manufacturer, ______________________ was producing cars in 1901 which sold for $650. His success attracted others to the infant automobile industry and helped to make the automobile popular with the public.

15. A pioneer in radio broadcasting, ______________________ obtained patents on more than 300 inventions. His vacuum tube, patented in 1907, was basic to the development of long-distance radio and television communication, and has often been called as great an invention as the radio itself.

Lesson 17

A Marriage Proposal

Words for Study

meditates	decades	architect	famine
palpitation	peculiar	glutton	tuberculosis
gorgeously	intriguer	disciplinarian	currency
inherited	dipsomaniac	vulgar	unabridged

A Marriage Proposal

by Anton Chekhov

One change that has been particularly popular with writers throughout the centuries is a change of heart. In this excerpt from a one-act play by the Russian writer Anton Chekhov, note the changes in the characters' attitudes and the reasons for them.

* * *

Scene: The reception room in Stepan Stepanovitch Tscubukov's home. Ivan Vassiliyitch Lomov enters, wearing a dress suit.

Stepan: (*going toward Ivan and greeting him*) Who is this I see? My dear fellow! Ivan Vassiliyitch! I'm so glad to see you! (*Shakes hands*) But this is a surprise! How are you?

Ivan: Thank you! And how are you?

Stepan: Oh, so-so, my friend. Please sit down. It isn't right to forget one's neighbor. But tell me, why all this ceremony? Dress clothes, white gloves and all? Are you on your way to some engagement, my good fellow?

Ivan: No, I have no engagement except with you, Stepan Stepanovitch.

Stepan: But why in evening clothes, my friend? This isn't New Year's!

Ivan: You see, it's simply this, that—(*composing himself*) I have come to you, Stepan Stepanovitch, to trouble you with a request. It is not the first time I have had the honor of turning to you for assistance, and you have always, that is—I beg your pardon, I am a bit excited! I'll take a drink of water first, dear Stepan Stepanovitch. (*He drinks.*)

Stepan: (*aside*) He's come to borrow money! I won't give him any! (*To Ivan*) What is it then, dear Lomov?

Ivan: You see—dear—Stepanovitch, pardon me, Stepan—Stepan—dearvitch—I mean—I am terribly nervous, as you will be so good as to see—! What I mean to say—you are the only one who can help me, though I don't deserve it, and—and I have no right whatever to make this request of you.

Stepan: Oh, don't beat about the bush, my dear fellow. Tell me!

Ivan: Immediately—in a moment. Here it is, then: I have come to ask for the hand of your daughter, Natalia Stepanovna.

Stepan: (*joyfully*) Angel! Ivan Vassiliyitch! Say that once again! I didn't quite hear it!

Ivan: I have the honor to beg—

Stepan: (*interrupting*) My dear, dear man! I am so happy that everything is so—everything! (*Embraces and kisses him*) I have wanted this to happen for so long. It has been my dearest wish! (*He represses a tear.*) And I have always loved you, my dear fellow, as my own son! May God give you His blessings and His grace and—I always wanted it to happen. But why am I standing here like a blockhead? I am completely dumbfounded with pleasure, completely dumbfounded. My whole being—I'll call Natalia—

Ivan: Dear Stepan Stepanovitch, what do you think? May I hope for Natalia Stepanovna's acceptance?

Stepan: Really! A fine boy like you—and you think she won't accept on the minute? Lovesick as a cat and all that—! (*He goes out.*)

Ivan: I'm cold. My whole body is trembling as though I was going to take my examination! But the chief thing is to settle matters! If a person meditates too much, or hesitates, or talks about it, waits for an ideal or for true love, he never gets it. Brrr! It's cold! Natalia is an excellent housekeeper, not at all bad looking, well educated—what more could I ask? I'm so excited my ears are roaring! (*He drinks water.*) And not to marry, that won't do! In the first place, I'm thirty-five—a critical age, you might say. In the second place, I must live a well-regulated life. I have a weak heart, continual palpitation, and I am very sensitive and always getting excited. My lips begin to tremble and the pulse in my right temple throbs terribly. But the worst of all is sleep! I hardly lie down and begin to doze before something in my left side begins to pull and tug, and something begins to hammer in my left shoulder—and in my head, too! I jump up like a madman, walk about a little, lie down again, but the moment I fall asleep I have a terrible cramp in the side. And so it is all night long!

(*Enter Natalia Stepanovna.*)

Natalia: Ah! It's you. Papa said to go in: there was a dealer in there who'd come to buy something. Good afternoon, Ivan Vassiliyitch.

Ivan: Good day, my dear Natalia Stepanovna.

Natalia: You must pardon me for wearing my apron and this old dress: we are working today. Why haven't you come to see us more often? You've not been here for so long! Sit down. (*They sit down.*) Won't you have something to eat?

Ivan: Thank you, I have just had lunch.

Natalia: Smoke, do, there are the matches. Today it is beautiful and only yesterday it rained so hard that the workmen couldn't do a stroke of work. How many bricks have you cut? Think of it! I was so anxious that I had the whole field mowed, and now I'm sorry I did it, because I'm afraid the hay will rot. It would have been better if I had waited. But what on earth is this? You are in evening clothes! The latest cut! Are you on your way to a ball? And you seem to be looking better, too—really. Why are you dressed up so gorgeously?

Ivan: (*excited*) You see, my dear Natalia Stepanovna—it's simply this: I have decided to ask you to listen to me—of course it will be a surprise, and indeed you'll be angry, but I—(*Aside*). How fearfully cold it is!

Natalia: What is it? (*A pause*) Well?

Ivan: I'll try to be brief. My dear Natalia Stepanovna, as you know, for many years, since my childhood, I have had the honor to know your family. My poor aunt and her husband, from whom, as you know, I inherited the estate, always had the greatest respect for your father and your poor mother. The Lomovs and the Tscubukovs have been for decades on the friendliest, indeed the closest, terms with each other, and furthermore my property, as you know, adjoins your own. If you will be so good as to remember, my meadows touch your birch woods.

Natalia: Pardon the interruption. You said "my meadows"—but are they yours?

Ivan: Yes, they belong to me.

Natalia: What nonsense! The meadows belong to us—not to you!

Ivan: No, to me! Now, my dear Natalia Stepanovna!

Natalia: Well, that is certainly news to me. How do they belong to you?

Ivan: How? I am speaking of the meadows lying between your birch woods and my brick-earth.

Natalia: Yes, exactly. They belong to us.

Ivan: No, you are mistaken, my dear Natalia Stepanovna, they belong to me. It is all a matter of record, my dear Natalia Stepanovna. It is true that at one time the title to the meadows was disputed, but now everyone knows they belong to me. There is no room for discussion. Be so good as to listen: my aunt's grandmother put these meadows, free from all costs, into the hands of your father's father's grandfather's peasants for a certain time while they were making bricks for my grandmother. These people used the meadows free of cost for about forty years, living there as they would on their own property. Later, however, when—

Natalia: There's not a word of truth in that!

Ivan: I'll show you the papers, Natalia Stepanovna.

Natalia: No, either you are joking, or trying to lead me into a discussion. That's not at all nice! We have owned this property for nearly three hundred years, and now all at once we hear that it doesn't belong to us. Ivan Vassiliyitch, you will pardon me, but I really can't believe my ears. So far as I am concerned, the meadows are worth very little. In all they don't contain more than five acres and they are worth only a few hundred roubles, say three hundred, but the injustice of the thing is what affects me. Say what you will, I can't bear injustice.

Ivan: Only listen until I have finished, please!

Natalia: And if you keep on explaining it for two days, and put on five suits of evening clothes, the meadows are still ours, ours, ours! I don't want to take your property, but I refuse to give up what belongs to us!

Ivan: Natalia Stepanovna, I don't need the meadows, I am only concerned with the principle. If you are agreeable, I beg of you, accept them as a gift from me!

Natalia: But I can give them to you, because they belong to me! That is very peculiar, Ivan Vassiliyitch! Until now we have considered you as a good neighbor and a good friend; only last year we lent you our threshing machine so that we couldn't thresh until November, and now you treat us like thieves! You offer to give me my own land. Excuse me, but neighbors don't treat each other that way. In my opinion, it's a very low trick—to speak frankly—

Ivan: The meadows are mine, do you understand? Mine!

Natalia: Really, you needn't scream so! If you want to scream and snort and rage you may do it at home, but here please keep yourself within the limits of common decency.

Ivan: My dear lady, if it weren't that I were suffering from palpitation of the heart and hammering of the arteries in my temples, I would deal with you very differently! (*In a loud voice*) The meadows belong to me!

Natalia: Us!

Ivan: Me!

(*Enter Stepan.*)

Stepan: What's going on here? What is he yelling about?

Natalia: Papa, please tell this gentleman to whom the meadows belong, to us or to him?

Stepan: My dear fellow, the meadows are ours.

Ivan: But, merciful heavens, Stepan Stepanovitch, how do you make that out? You at least might be reasonable. My aunt's grandmother gave the use of the meadows free of cost to your grandfather's peasants; the peasants lived on the land for forty years and used it as their own, but later when—

Stepan: Permit me, my dear friend. You forget that your grandmother's peasants never paid, because there had been a lawsuit over the meadows, and everyone knows that the meadows belong to us. You haven't looked at the map.

Ivan: I'll prove to you that they belong to me!

Natalia: The meadows belong to us and I won't give them up! I won't give them up! I won't give them up!

Ivan: We'll see about that! I'll prove in court that they belong to me.

Stepan: In court! You may sue in court, sir, if you like! Oh, I know you, you are only waiting to find an excuse to go to law! You're an intriguer, that's what you are! Your whole family were always looking for quarrels. The whole lot!

Ivan: Kindly refrain from insulting my family. The entire race of Lomov has always been honorable! And never has one been brought to trial for embezzlement, as your dear uncle was!

Stepan: And the whole Lomov family were insane!

Natalia: Every one of them!

Stepan: Your grandmother was a dipsomaniac, and the younger aunt ran off with an architect.

Ivan: And your mother limped. (*He puts his hand over his heart*). Oh, my side pains! My temples are bursting! Lord in Heaven! Water!

Stepan: And your dear father was a gambler—and a glutton!

Natalia: And your aunt was a gossip like few others!

Ivan: And you are an intriguer. Oh, my heart! And it's an open secret that you cheated at the elections—my eyes are blurred! Where is my hat?

Natalia: Oh, how low! Liar! Disgusting thing!

Ivan: Where's the hat—? My heart! Where shall I go? Where is the door—? Oh—it seems—as though I were dying! I can't—my legs won't hold me—(*He goes to the door.*)

Stepan: (*following him*) May you never darken my door again!

Natalia: Bring your suit to court! We'll see! (*Lomov staggers out.*)

Stepan: (*angrily*) The devil!

Natalia: Such a good-for-nothing! And then they talk about being good neighbors!

Stepan: Loafer! Scarecrow! Monster!

Natalia: A swindler like that takes over a piece of property that doesn't belong to him and then dares to argue about it!

Stepan: And to think that this fool dares to make a proposal of marriage!

Natalia: What? A proposal of marriage?

Stepan: Why, yes! He came here to make you a proposal of marriage.

Natalia: Why didn't you tell me that before?

Stepan: That's why he had on his evening clothes! The poor fool!

Natalia: Proposal for me? Oh! (*Falls into an armchair and groans*) Bring him back! Bring him back!

Stepan: Bring whom back?

Natalia: Faster, faster, I'm sinking! Bring him back! (*She becomes hysterical.*)

Stepan: What is it? What's wrong with you? I'm cursed with bad luck! I'll shoot myself! I'll hang myself!

Natalia: I'm dying! Bring him back!

Stepan: Bah! In a minute! Don't bawl! (*He rushes out.*)

Natalia: (*groaning*) What have they done to me? Bring him back! Bring him back!

Stepan: (*Comes running in*) He's coming at once! The devil take him! Ugh! Talk to him yourself, I can't.

Natalia: (*groaning*) Bring him back!

Stepan: He's coming, I tell you! Oh, Lord! What a task it is to be the father of a grown daughter!

From "A Marriage Proposal" by Anton Chekhov.

1 **Understanding the Play.** Answer the following questions in good sentence form.

1. What does Stepan *first* believe to be the reason for Ivan's visit?

2. What is the real reason for Ivan's visit?

3. Why do Ivan and Natalia begin to quarrel?

4. Does their argument pertain to serious or trivial matters? Be sure to include evidence from the play to support your answer.

5. How does Ivan intend to resolve the quarrel?

6. Why does Natalia soon regret Ivan's sudden departure?

7. Why does Stepan remark, "What a task it is to be the father of a grown daughter"?

8. Do you think this play is intended to be *serious* or *humorous*? Cite evidence from the play which supports your answer.

2 **You Be the Playwright.** The scene you have just read is only the first part of a one-act play. Based on what you have learned about the characters thus far, write a relatively detailed description of how you think the play should end. If you wish, use your own paper to actually write the dialogue. If you include stage directions, be sure to enclose them in parentheses.

3 **More about Anton Chekhov.** Use the words listed at the left to complete these sentences correctly.

monotony
monotonous
monotonously

1. Anton Chekhov, the author of "A Marriage Proposal," was born in 1860 in a province in southern Russia where many of the townspeople complained ________________ about the ________________ of their lives, which must have made their daily routines seem even more ________________.

inspired
uninspired
inspiration

2. ________________ by his life in the small town, Anton found his ________________ in swimming and fishing. On one of his outings, he became quite ill and was nursed back to health by a kindly doctor who is said to have ________________ the young Chekhov's own choice of a medical career.

severe
severely
severity

3. Known for his ________________, his father, who was a grocer, ________________ scolded his six children for wrongdoings; but Anton's brother wrote that their father was ________________ only when absolutely necessary and beat the children only in "exceptional cases."

reliably
unreliable
reliability

4. Although Anton's father was ________________ strict as a disciplinarian, he was ________________ as a grocer. After he went bankrupt, the family moved to Moscow where they counted on Anton's strength and ________________ to pull them through their hardships.

wretched
wretchedly
wretchedness

5. In the 1880s, Chekhov began to write plays which, at first, audiences found ________________ immature. But since he was his own worst critic Chekhov always had the last word on ________________, and he described his successful one-act play "A Marriage Proposal" as "a ________________, vulgar, boring little skit."

irritate irritation irritable	6. Actors and actresses could ________________ Chekhov a great deal. Actresses, whom he described as cows, made him ________________, and his ________________ with actors caused him to state that they should never be allowed to speak their opinions because they were so boring.
censor censorship uncensored	7. Another nuisance for Chekhov was ________________. The duty of a ________________ was to tone down material that might provoke thought. *Famine*, for example, which was a very stark reality for many Russian people, was supposed to be called a "temporary food shortage," and Chekhov was astonished when this word remained ________________ in one of his stories.
modest modesty immodest	8. Chekhov may have been ________________ in his remarks, but he reacted with utmost ________________ to the fact that, by the late 1880s, he was honored as a national celebrity even though the income from his plays and stories was still quite ________________ and barely covered his expenses.
mortal mortally immortal immortality	9. In 1904, Chekhov lay ________________ ill from tuberculosis, a disease that had plagued his ________________ being for many years. As his wife pressed an ice pack against his heart, Chekhov perhaps realized his writing might achieve ________________ but that he himself was not ________________, for he remarked to his wife, "You don't put ice on an empty heart."

4 **Synonym Review.** From the choices given, choose the best synonym for the word in bold-faced type and write it on the line to the right.

1. **hazard:**	complication	danger	detour	setback	______
2. **basis:**	figment	foundation	hearth	objective	______
3. **meditate:**	determine	fascinate	ponder	profess	______
4. **reap:**	cultivate	harvest	shuck	sow	______
5. **intrigue:**	fantasy	imposition	motive	scheme	______
6. **interval:**	extension	pause	postponement	recurrence	______
7. **flexible:**	adaptable	motivated	objective	vigorous	______
8. **ascend:**	circumvent	climb	elevate	hoist	______
9. **tendency:**	conception	instinct	leaning	motivation	______
10. **prestige:**	dedication	influence	precedence	profession	______
11. **elegant:**	enormous	expressive	honorable	splendid	______
12. **domestic:**	household	personal	professional	public	______
13. **arduous:**	alien	difficult	dishonorable	unreasonable	______
14. **palpitate:**	cascade	collapse	dilate	flutter	______
15. **blatant:**	contradictory	distorted	improbable	obvious	______
16. **flux:**	abundance	flow	tremor	vigor	______

5 **Foreign Currency.** In "A Marriage Proposal," the characters spoke of the worth of the meadow in terms of *roubles*, the basic unit of currency in Russia. With the help of a dictionary, match the currencies listed in the left column with the correct country. (Hint: In most unabridged dictionaries, the entries *currency* or *money* provide this information.)

deutsche mark
dollar
drachma
franc
guilder
krone
lira
mark
peseta
peso
pound
rupee
yen
yuan

________________ 1. Australia

________________ 2. China

________________ 3. Denmark

________________ 4. East Germany

________________ 5. France

________________ 6. Greece

________________ 7. India

________________ 8. Italy

________________ 9. Japan

________________ 10. Mexico

________________ 11. Netherlands

________________ 12. Spain

________________ 13. United Kingdom

________________ 14. West Germany

Lesson 18

The Significance of Change

Words for Study

anxiety	sufficient	assuredly	observant
external	optimist	motivation	immersion
corrupt	voluntarily	naught	Hindu
scoff	magnified	evaluating	pessimist

The Significance of Change

In this reading, Leo Buscaglia discusses why many people are so unhappy in today's world and suggests that by changing their attitudes toward change, people create in themselves the power to change their lives.

* * *

People are forever expressing their loneliness, despair, frustration, and loss of hope. In day-to-day living they find it difficult to share, to understand, and to relate to others. They feel that they must cope with an unreasonable amount of envy, fear, anxiety, and hate. They are constantly finding reasons for their unhappiness in those around them and in their external environment: "The political system is corrupt and will always be so." "Wars are inevitable." "Man is essentially evil and cannot change." "Justice, peace, and security are only for the wealthy; the common man is just a dupe of the system." "Education is meaningless for the future." "Existence is a dead-end street where death stands holding a bloody knife. There are no detours, no escapes."

People see themselves as helpless in a situation that is hopeless. They appear intent upon looking for gloom. They seem more willing to accept the negative than the positive, always more prepared to doubt than trust. They are continually living in worry about the future and disappointment regarding the past. They seldom find themselves as the source of their unhappiness. They scoff at the idea that they can also elect happiness.

Yet, in fact, human beings may be the only living creatures with sufficient will and intelligence to choose happiness. How sad that they so often choose despair. Indeed, an optimist is seen as a fool. A lover is seen as a helpless romantic. If one enjoys life, he is called a "ne'er-do-well." There is the general feeling that if one is joyful today, he is certain to be punished for it tomorrow. The popular saying, "All that's good in the world is either illegal, immoral, or fattening," is but one example of the type of negative thinking that colors so much of our daily living.

We seldom question the fact that ugliness and evil are to be found in the world. But we're never as ready to accept the fact that life also offers unlimited beauty and potential for joy, as well as endless opportunities for pleasure.

People become dissatisfied with themselves and then place the blame on the aspects of their lives that they cannot alter in order to give themselves a sense of comfort. In this way, they relieve themselves of all responsibility.

I am not suggesting that there is no evil in the world, nothing to fear, no corruption, no hatred. People need only to pick up any newspaper, watch any television screen, read any modern novel, or follow the world political scene to find all the unpleasantness and injustice they need to reinforce a negative attitude.

We tend to suspect people of evil more readily than of good. The evil in the world makes the news media, the good seldom does. When a crime occurs, we are certain to hear of it. In reality, however, the greater number of people are like ourselves. They do not voluntarily hurt another human being, steal from him, or kill him. They can usually be trusted, are concerned, and are friendly. Most people live their lives without having to deal with police, courts of law, or lawyers. This fact is regarded as what is to be expected of people. The evil people do, however, is magnified. It is of interest because it is the exception. But we act, often, as if the exception is the rule.

Perhaps the greatest tribute to the good in people was paid by the young Anne Frank, a Jewish girl who literally spent most of her short life hiding from the Nazis in a small apartment in Amsterdam and finally met her death at their hands. She was still able to write in her diary shortly before her murder: "No matter. I still believe that at heart man is good."

People learn to perceive evil in the same way that they learn to perceive good. If people believe in a world of evil, they will respond to what they see in a suspicious, fearful manner. They will constantly be searching for and assuredly finding the evil they seek. If, on the other hand, people believe in a world of good, they will remain confident and hopeful in their attitude toward living, learning, and change.

One might question whether or not people can change the way in which they view the world in which they live—if they can change their attitudes toward change itself. The answer is *yes*.

Human beings can learn, relearn, or unlearn to the point of death. There is always more to discover. No matter how much knowledge people have, they can never know everything about anything. For this reason, one student of language has said that all sentences should end with "etc."

Change is the end result of all true learning. Change involves three things: First, a dissatisfaction with oneself—a felt void or need; second, a decision to change—to fill the void or need; and third, a conscious dedication to the process of growth and change—the willful act of making the change, of doing something.

Most people fail to consider the power and force of one's attitude and will in the complicated process of change. Certainly people must contend with the external forces, the natural forces. An earthquake, flood, or bolt of lightning may destroy them or those they love. An accident may permanently cripple them.

But how people respond, react, and live with the handicap or through the earthquake or flood is another matter. This they can regulate. This they have some management over. People have will and thus, to a large measure, can guide their lives.

Also, the destructive effects of external forces are not often experienced in one's lifetime. Thus, people are free to use their internal powers to make their own lives. They can write their own dialogue, surround themselves with the actors of their choice, paint their backdrop, and arrange their background music. Then, if they don't like the play they have created for themselves, they have only themselves to blame. But even then they have a choice. They can get off the stage and produce a new play. Free people are free even in the darkest prison.

Most people in despair have little knowledge and less will with which to make things better for themselves. They are convinced that things cannot be altered. Yet, as long as they have will, they do in fact have some degree of control over their reactions, responses, and conclusions. To this extent they can assume responsibility for their own lives. They are not totally at the mercy of forces greater than themselves, for they themselves become a powerful force.

In order to change, then, people must trust that they are capable of change. If they are dissatisfied with their abilities, they must face this fact but be convinced that they are able to do something about it.

When change confronts a person, he often uses the excuse that he is too old to change, too old to learn. He says, "You can't teach an old dog new tricks." Yet even an "old dog" can learn new tricks. The real issue is that the person may lack motivation or simply be lazy. Man's ability to learn will always be greater than that of the "old dog," and to compare them is to degrade the very strength that keeps a dog a dog but makes a person a human being.

Knowing that one is always capable of change, the second step lies in making the decision to change. Change does not occur by merely willing it any more than behavior changes simply through insight. One can know that something is evil, painful, or dangerous and still pursue it with determination.

People can only move toward change when they willfully arrive at a proposal to do so. For example, an overweight gentleman who wants desperately to be slim and handsome in his bathing suit cannot do it by desire alone. He must plan a proper diet, stay on his diet, and engage in the right exercise. Otherwise, his wish will never become a reality. He may have insight about how to achieve his goal; but until the moment of action, all of his insight goes for naught. "To be is to do," says one philosopher. "One only becomes real, or human, at the point of action."

The third step in change is perhaps the most difficult. It involves the actual processes of the relearning. All learning involves searching, finding, analyzing, evaluating, experiencing, accepting, rejecting, practice, and reinforcement.

As in learning all things, you must be constantly alert, watchful, patient, observant, trusting, open-minded, and not easily discouraged. You must be willing to experiment and be constantly evaluating and flexible. Life and the experiences that come from a total immersion in living offer the best classroom for learning. Even the greatest teachers cannot give you wisdom. They can only help by guiding you, by offering insights, suggestions, and encouragement. You will not learn by watching others live, either; you will only learn as an active participant.

It is good if one is dissatisfied with himself for it may be the first step in the process of change. But it is only a beginning. One must also will to change and act to change. Learning is a complicated, lifelong process. To learn is to be in constant change. The process is endless.

Each day we are offered new means for learning and growing, and growing, learning, and experiencing involve change. Change is inevitable. There is only one thing of which you can be certain and that is change. To deny change is to deny the only single reality. Attitudes change, feelings change, desires change.

There is no stopping change, no holding it back; there is only going with it. There is a Hindu tale about a man in a small boat rowing up a fast-flowing river against the current. After a great battle, he finally discovers that the effort is useless, so he gives up, raises his oars and begins to sing. The moment teaches him a new way of life; only when he goes with the changing river is a person truly free.

Adapted from *Love* by Leo Buscaglia. New York: Fawcett Crest Books, 1972. Used by permission of the author.

1 **Understanding the Reading.** Put the letter of the best answer on the line to the left.

_____ 1. Which of the following does Buscaglia consider to be inevitable?
(a) change (c) negativity
(b) learning (d) wars

_____ 2. According to Buscaglia, the source of most unhappiness is _____.
(a) fate (c) our upbringing
(b) ourselves (d) the world

_____ 3. Buscaglia uses the example of people's belief that "existence is a dead-end street" to make the point that _____.
(a) despair is a common response to life
(b) happiness demands a price
(c) the media have an impact on our lives
(d) man is essentially evil

_____ 4. In comparing life to a play, Buscaglia compares us to the _____.
(a) audience (c) playwright
(b) cast (d) stage manager

_____ 5. According to Buscaglia, many of the tragedies we experience can be controlled in terms of how we _____.
(a) diagnose them (c) prepare for them
(b) obscure them (d) respond to them

_____ 6. The example of the overweight gentleman is used to emphasize the point that one must _____.
(a) be self-confident in order to change
(b) exercise caution if he weighs too much
(c) form a plan of action and execute it
(d) not try to lose weight too quickly

_____ 7. Buscaglia cites the example of the Hindu tale to emphasize that _____ is the least helpful response to change.
(a) despair (c) resistance
(b) knowledge (d) surrender

_____ 8. According to Buscaglia, the best classroom for learning is provided by _____.
(a) change (c) life
(b) good teachers (d) suffering

2 **Optimists and Pessimists.** An *optimist* looks on the brighter side of any situation. His opposite—the *pessimist*—has eyes only for the gloomy side. In summing up the difference between these two types of people, one poet remarked, "An optimist sees the doughnut, but a pessimist sees the hole." Decide how each type of person might respond to the following sentences taken from the reading and write your answers in the space provided. The first one is done to get you started.

1. "Man is essentially evil and cannot change."

   a. Optimist: I believe there is good in all men and that even evil men can change.

   b. Pessimist: I agree wholeheartedly with the statement.

2. "...human beings may be the only living creatures with sufficient will and intelligence to choose happiness."

   a. Optimist: ______________________________

   b. Pessimist: ______________________________

3. "They (people) can usually be trusted, are concerned, and are friendly."

   a. Optimist: ______________________________

   b. Pessimist: ______________________________

4. "A free man is free even in the darkest prison."

   a. Optimist: ______________________________

   b. Pessimist: ______________________________

5. "There is only one thing of which you can be certain and that is change."

   a. Optimist: ______________________________

   b. Pessimist: ______________________________

3 **Antonym Review.** From the choices listed, choose the best antonym for the word in bold-faced type and write it on the line to the right.

1. **suspicious:**	indifferent	reckless	trusting	wary	________
2. **involuntary:**	attentive	meditated	predictable	willful	________
3. **scoff:**	concur	envision	praise	retort	________
4. **centralize:**	disentangle	dismember	dismiss	disperse	________
5. **accustomed:**	arduous	consistent	inflexible	unusual	________
6. **irritable:**	pleasant	pretentious	reliable	stately	________
7. **domestic:**	elegant	foreign	modest	national	________
8. **corruption:**	integrity	intrigue	mortality	prestige	________
9. **peculiar:**	civilized	commonplace	instinctive	tiresome	________
10. **inattentive:**	dissatisfied	efficient	glaring	observant	________
11. **vulgar:**	costly	economical	gorgeous	refined	________
12. **anxiety:**	consistency	elegance	negativity	security	________
13. **pessimistic:**	adaptable	optimistic	prosperous	unknowing	________
14. **hazardous:**	exposed	permissible	primitive	safe	________
15. **gluttony:**	abstinence	caution	perfection	virtue	________

4 **Signs of Change.** Match the changes at the right with the person who would be most likely to recognize them.

ambassador
ecologist
economist
grocer
mayor
missionary
navigator
psychologist
sociologist
tutor

_______________ 1. a decrease in trash along a highway

_______________ 2. a patient's improved mental health

_______________ 3. changes in social patterns

_______________ 4. changes in a student's study habits

_______________ 5. a sudden change in a ship's course

_______________ 6. increased international tensions

_______________ 7. pressure for better public services

_______________ 8. soaring wholesale food prices

_______________ 9. increased support for religious activities

_______________ 10. the lowering of interest rates

5 **An Inventor's Advice.** One person who thrived on change and was always eager to change both himself and social conditions for the better was Benjamin Franklin. One of his famous sayings can be found by solving this puzzle. Refer to Exercise 5 in Lesson 3 if you have forgotten how to do this type of puzzle. The first one has been done to get you started.

KAYOS ○ ____	LATER ○ ____	MONAD ○ ____	SMALL ○ ____	EXIST ○ ____	= 65
TUTOR ○ ____	FIRED ○ ____	SLIDE ○ ____	YEMEN ○ ____	PAGES ○ ____	= 65
CHASE ○ ____	NOBLE ○ ____	SEVER ○ ____	MANOR ○ ____	STRUT ○ ____	= 65
ZONED ○ ____	LEASE ○ ____	DOORS ○ ____	REINS ○ ____	MITES ○ ____	= 65
SETUP ○ ____	CURBS ○ ____	ALLOY (1) LOYAL	RUNES ○ ____	TRINE ○ ____	= 65
= 65	= 65	= 65	= 65	= 65	

✓1. Faithful; trustworthy
2. Agrees to; endorses
3. To clean vigorously
4. A freshwater fish
5. Confidence; faith; reliance
6. Details; bits of information
7. Shopping centers
8. Departs; takes off
9. Runs an engine in neutral
10. A fire engine's alarm
11. The inventor of dynamite
12. An artist's stand
13. Poetry
14. A synonym for foe
15. A citizen of Italy's capital city
16. Cooked in hot oil or fat
17. Smells; scents
18. Disturbed; distressed; bothered
19. A hospital employee
20. Twelve items
21. Pains; hurts
22. Stares
23. Watchful; attentive
24. Lifeless; inactive
25. A wanderer

Benjamin Franklin's words of advice:

L _ _ _   _ _ _ _   _ _   _ _ _ _ _   _ _ _ _ _   _ _ _ _ _.

1 2 3 4   5 6 7 8   9 10   11 12 13 14 15   16 17 18 19 20   21 22 23 24 25

Lesson 19

It's Good to Be Alive

Words for Study

ignition	quadriplegics	minority	rehabilitation
ceramics	paraplegics	integration	Confederate
kiln	equality	savvy	infirmity

It's Good to Be Alive

Voted the National League's Most Valuable Player in 1951, 1953, and 1955, Roy Campanella served as catcher for the Brooklyn Dodgers baseball team for 10 years. In this excerpt from his autobiography *It's Good to Be Alive*, "Campy" describes one of the most painful changes a person can experience and what this change has meant in his life.

* * *

What stands out most in my mind of all that has happened since the fateful morning of January 28, 1958, when the world turned upside down for me, was something that happened at Holman Stadium in Vero Beach, Florida, nearly fourteen months after my accident.

From where I was sitting in my wheelchair, I could see this little crippled old lady struggling up the steep ramp. She wore steel braces on both legs. Slowly she made her way up with the aid of a wooden crutch under her right arm. Her left arm hung loosely at her side, paralyzed. Her snow-white head was tilted slightly to the left.

Her attendant, a middle-aged man, walked slowly alongside, ever on the alert to grab her should she stumble or fall. Once or twice he tried to assist her, but she shrugged him off. She finally made the top of the ramp where I was sitting. She was gasping and out of breath. She opened her mouth to speak; but no words came. She stood there looking at me in the chair. Her eyes, sorrowed by years of suffering, looked down on my paralyzed body. She slowly lifted them to my face. Reaching out an old, thinned right arm, she took my limp hand in hers.

"Mr. Campanella," she finally managed to say, "I came a long, long way to see you. More than a thousand miles. I just had to see you and thank you, for you gave me the courage and the will to go on when everything seemed hopeless." Her voice trailed off. She was all spent from the excitement, the long trip, the steep climb, the deep emotion. She was very old, and she must have weighed all of eighty-five or ninety pounds. Who was she? Why had she made this long trip? Had she really come just to see me? I wanted to say something to her as she stood there looking down at me, barely able to stand up and refusing to support herself on the arm of her attendant. Then I saw she was ready to speak again.

"Oh, I'm so glad I came," she said earnestly. "You see, I was a patient in the same hospital with you in New York. At the same time. I had a stroke and my entire left side became paralyzed. I couldn't even talk. They didn't give me much hope. As for me, I didn't care whether I made it or not. Then you were brought in. The people at the hospital said you had no chance to live. Crushed vertebrae. A broken neck.

"But you did live. The doctors marveled at your courage. They were thrilled with your faith. They set you up as the example, the inspiration. You became a symbol.

The Bettmann Archive

"I don't know exactly when I stopped giving up. All I know is that one day I decided that I just didn't want to stop yet. I was determined to get back on my feet. It was you who gave me the courage, the will to live."

I sat there without saying a word. I just couldn't find any. I've never been accused of being the quiet, shy type. I'm a firm believer in free speech. But that was one time when my tongue was stuck in my mouth. It was most embarrassing. I wanted to thank her. I wanted to ask her name; find out where she was from; learn whether she had any children. But all I could think of was that this wonderful little crippled old lady had come down the length of the United States just to say hello to me—me, Roy Campanella, a Negro ballplayer who happened to have an accident that ended his career and maybe put him for the rest of his life in a wheelchair....

I'm a lucky guy. I've got so much to be thankful for. Don't feel sorry for me. Please. I'm on my way back, and I'm going to make it.

Some people may think the Lord turned his back on me because of the accident. That's not so. I consider myself very lucky that I was able to play ball for twenty years, half of them in the big leagues. And even when I had the accident I was lucky. How many people have similar accidents and are killed? I could have been burned up in that automobile, and I could have died in the hospital after I got pneumonia. The car turned over on me and the engine was running for I don't know how long. The gasoline could easily have leaked out and caught fire, and I couldn't have done anything about it. I tried to turn off the ignition with my left hand. I couldn't move my arm. I couldn't move anything. That's when I knew my whole body was paralyzed.

I have made a great deal of progress. I'm going to make more. There was a time when I couldn't move my arms or my head, when I couldn't sit up. For many months after the accident I couldn't use my hands at all. I couldn't eat or drink by myself. Now I can do all those things. Each day I feel stronger and every day I try something new.

It doesn't take too much fight if you have the courage and the faith. All of us want to live and I'm one of them. And I hope to continue to live and maybe to help some others in the same condition who may have given up just a little.

Until January 28, 1958, I was a ballplayer whose aim, then at least, was to catch one more full season with the Dodgers. After that, well, maybe I could turn to coaching. Baseball was my world. In many ways that still goes. Today I'm still an ex-ballplayer whose life centers around the game, but I know that I'm something else too. Because, where before I might have been a fellow with a fair understanding of life, today I understand a great deal more about many more things — especially this wonderful thing called the human spirit. And so, while this accident made me a cripple, it also made me a better human. And please don't chalk that up to saying "Campy's preaching." I ain't.

And don't think this is the kind of thing you can learn without working at it and some pain to boot.

Beginning from the time of my accident, and for the best part of a year, I knew what it is to be real sick. Fearful sick. And I was a long ways from being out of the woods, so to speak, for some time after I was moved to the Institute. I was scared and I hurt all over and, like I said, there were times when I dreaded facing the possibility that I was broken so bad I might not be able to support my family or myself any longer. That was the worst fear. But I didn't want to show this fear to Dr. Rusk or the wonderful man that he assigned to my case, Dr. Edward Lowman.

One day when my wife Ruthe was sitting there and trying to keep my mind off myself, she said, "Campy, Dr. Lowman talked to me today about you."

"Yeah?" I replied, hardly listening. "What did he have to say?"

"He says that he has yet to see you depressed —really depressed. That worries him. He says that if a patient doesn't show his sorry thoughts, but keeps them bottled up inside, it can be a bad sign. He wanted to know if you ever break down a little and let go when we're alone here."

"What did you tell him?" I asked.

"I told him the truth. I said, 'Yes, Doctor, Campy's had quite a few bad sessions when we've been alone. He still does.' Dr. Lowman was pleased to hear that."

Several days later, Dr. Rusk stopped by my room. After we'd talked about anything and everything except my condition, he said, "Campy, I know what you're thinking, and I think I know what you're asking yourself. You're asking the old question: Why must I suffer? It's possible that the answer to that is in the work of the potter. You see, Campy, great ceramics are not made by putting clay in the sun. They only come from the white heat of the kiln. In the firing process, some pieces are broken. But those that survive the heat are transformed from clay into objects of art."

It wasn't until several weeks later, after I began to take my place in the hospital community, that I began to understand Dr. Rusk's words better. Quadriplegics or paraplegics, we've all suffered—not only in body but in mind. We've been through the white heat of that kiln. But due to that torture—and it is torture—I think that maybe we have a bond of understanding that goes below any surface stuff. So, in a sense then, we have not wasted our pain.

One day, while I was rolling through the halls of the Institute in my chair, I heard Dr. Rusk talking to someone in his office. To this day I don't know whether that person was a man or a woman, a reporter or a businessman, or even a patient. But I did hear him tell that person: "...People have such strength and potential, and more when they're paralyzed. Once they get over that hump, successfully pass through that first bad depression, they are better, spiritually, than ever before! These quadriplegics and paraplegics have such spirit as a well person can never understand."

Dr. Rusk was referring to me and thousands more like me. But it took me a lot of time to understand and appreciate the truth behind that statement. Today, however, I know those aren't just words.

All my life I have fought, in my own way, for equality, integration and understanding of minority groups. But from here on, I've taken on an even bigger job—fighting for the equality, integration, and understanding and acceptance of the severely handicapped.

We're a rugged breed, us quads. If we weren't, we wouldn't be around today. Yes, we're a rugged breed; and, in many ways, we've been blessed with a savvy and spirit that isn't given to everybody.

Today, if I am a life member of this rugged breed, I've also got a lot of people on my team. Thanks to the unseen army of medical men and women all over the world now striving to learn—well, some day maybe, I'll get out of this chair and walk again with my youngsters! So far, there's no way medical science knows to make a severed or a badly damaged spinal cord heal and function. But I've got to keep that hope! And I intend to hold onto it. While a quad never wants total acceptance of his condition, he does want understanding of what's wrong with him. Cancer patients are in the same boat with us—maybe more so. They also have hope that one day—maybe tomorrow, maybe next week, maybe next year—another human, or team of humans, will come through with a cure for their disease.

And let me say that this refusal of total or full acceptance of his disability all hooks up with one thing—*Faith*, an almost divine faith.

Down in the reception room of the Institute of Physical Medicine and Rehabilitation, over on the East River at 400 East 34th Street in New York City, there is a bronze plaque that's riveted to the wall. During the months of coming back to the Institute for treatment—two or three times a week—I rolled through that reception room many times, coming and going. But I never quite made the time to pull over to one side and read the words on that plaque that were written, it's said, by an unknown Confederate soldier. Then one afternoon last May, I did. I read it, and then I read it again. When I finished it the second time I was near to bursting—not in despair, but with an inner glow that had me straining to grip the arms of my wheelchair.

Here it is:

A Creed For Those Who Have Suffered

I asked God for strength, that I might achieve
  I was made weak, that I might learn humbly to obey...

I asked for health, that I might do greater things
  I was given infirmity, that I might do better things...

I asked for riches, that I might be happy
  I was given poverty that I might be wise...

I asked for power that I might have the praise of men
  I was given weakness, that I might feel the need of God...

I asked for all things that I might enjoy life
  I was given life, that I might enjoy all things...

I got nothing I asked for—but everything I had hoped for

Almost despite myself, my unspoken prayers were answered
  I am among men, most richly blessed!

No one could add anything to that.

1 **Understanding the Reading.** In good sentence form, explain the significance of the following for Roy Campanella.

1. The Dodgers: ______________________________

2. January 28, 1958: ______________________________

3. The woman who spoke to him at Holman Stadium: ______________________________

4. Twenty years: ______________________________

5. "great ceramics": ______________________________

6. "a rugged breed": ______________________________

7. The anonymous Confederate soldier: ______________________________

8. "I'm a lucky guy": ______________________________

2 **What Do You Think?** In brief paragraphs in which you include details or reasons to support your thoughts, answer the following questions.

1. In Latin, the word *finis* has two meanings: the end or finish, and a goal to reach. How do these two meanings relate to the excerpt from Roy Campanella's autobiography, and which meaning seems more appropriate to his philosophy?

2. When you find yourself confronted with a situation that involves personal suffering, how do the two meanings of *finis* relate to your experience, and which meaning seems more important to you?

3 **The Invention of Baseball.** Most people have been taught that the inventor of baseball was a man named Abner Doubleday. Yet here is a definition which appeared in *The Book of Sports*, published in 1834 when Doubleday was just 15 years old. Read this first recorded description of "the great American pastime" and then answer the questions which follow.

Base or Goal Ball. This game is known under a variety of names. It is sometimes called "round ball," but I believe that "base" or "goal ball" are the names generally adopted in our country. The players divide into two equal parties, and chance decides which shall have first innings. Four stones or stakes are placed from twelve to twenty yards asunder, as *A*, *B*, *C*, *D*, in the margin; another is put at *E*.

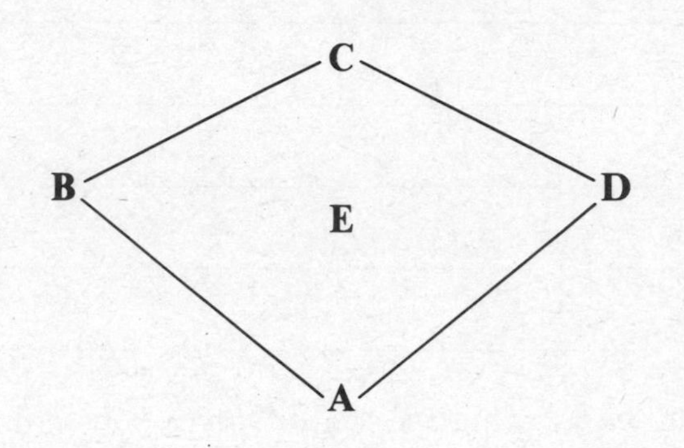

One of the party who is out places himself at *E*. He tosses the ball gently toward *A*, on the right of which one of the *in-party* places himself, and strikes the ball, if possible, with his bat. If he miss three times, or if the ball, when struck, be caught by any of the players of the opposite side who are scattered about the field, he is out, another takes his place. If none of these accidents take place, on striking the ball he drops the bat and runs toward *B*, or if he can, to *C*, *D* or even to *A* again. If, however, the boy who stands at *E*, or any of the outplayers who may happen to have the ball, strike him with it in his progress from *A* to *B*, *B* to *C*, *C* to *D*, or *D* to *A*, he is out. Supposing he can get only to *B*, one of his partners takes the bat, and strikes at the ball in turn. If the first player can get only to *C*, or *D*, the second runs to *B* only, or *C*, as the case may be, and a third player begins; as they get home, that is, to *A*, they play at the ball by turns, until they all get out. Then, of course, the outplayers take their places.

From: *The Man Who Invented Baseball* by Harold Peterson.

1. What is the term that we now use for "party"? ______________________

2. What is the term that we now use for "stones or stakes"? ______________________

3. What do the following stand for in the diagram?

   a. **E** - ____________________

   b. **A** - ____________________

   c. **B** - ____________________

   d. **D** - ____________________

4. Based on the context clues in the description, what does the word "asunder" mean?

   ____

5. What is the difference between how the pitcher was instructed to perform in 1834 and how he performs now?

   ____

   ____

6. How does the diagram help the reader to better understand this early description of baseball?

   ____

   ____

   ____

7. Draw a diagram of a modern-day baseball diamond in which you label each of the positions. If you don't follow baseball, get a baseball fan to help you.

4 **Change: Another Type of Response.** After you have read this poem by the American poet John Updike, answer the questions which follow.

Ex-Basketball Player
by John Updike

Pearl Avenue runs past the high-school lot,
Bends with the trolley tracks, and stops, cut off
Before it has a chance to go two blocks,
At Colonel McComsky Plaza. Berth's Garage
Is on the corner facing west, and there,
Most days, you'll find Flick Webb, who helps Berth out.

Flick stands tall among the idiot pumps—
Five on a side, the old bubble-head style,
Their rubber elbows hanging loose and low.
One's nostrils are two S's, and his eyes
An E and O.* And one is squat, without
A head at all—more of a football type.

Once Flick played for the high-school team, the Wizards.
He was good: in fact, the best. In '46,
He bucketed three hundred ninety points,
A county record still. The ball loved Flick.
I saw him rack up thirty-eight of forty
In one home game. His hands were like wild birds.

He never learned a trade, he just sells gas,
Checks oil, and changes flats. Once in a while,
As a gag, he dribbles an inner tube,
But most of us remember anyway.
His hands are fine and nervous on the lug wrench.
It makes no difference to the lug wrench, though.

Off work, he hangs around Mae's Luncheonette.
Grease-gray and kind of coiled, he plays pinball,
Sips lemon cokes, and smokes those thin cigars;
Flick seldom speaks to Mae, just sits and nods
Beyond her face towards bright applauding tiers
Of Necco Wafers, Nibs, and Juju Beads.

*Esso was a brand of gas

1. Roy Campanella and Flick Webb no longer play sports. Why did each stop playing?

2. What is the difference between how Roy Campanella and Flick Webb responded to this change?

3. What do you think accounts for the difference between Roy Campanella and Flick Webb?

4. Explain why you do or do not think Flick Webb's situation pertains only to athletes.

5. Explain who you think represents the more common reaction to change—Roy Campanella or Flick Webb—and why.

5 **Word Relationships.** On the line to the left, write the letter of the answer that best completes each statement.

_____ 1. Eastman is to photography as _____.
(a) automobile is to Olds
(b) Bell is to telegraphy
(c) Goodyear is to rubber
(d) Whitney is to mass production

_____ 2. Shuck is to corn as _____.
(a) pare is to apple
(b) rind is to grape
(c) pit is to cherry
(d) seed is to orange

_____ 3. Scoff is to jeer as _____.
(a) scatter is to dispel
(b) smirk is to snarl
(c) snort is to neigh
(d) swarm is to prey

_____ 4. Drachma is to Greece as _____.
(a) Deutsche mark is to East Germany
(b) krone is to Denmark
(c) peseta is to Mexico
(d) yuan is to Japan

_____ 5. Tuberculosis is to disease as _____.
(a) embezzlement is to felony
(b) bathtub is to immersion
(c) footstool is to gadget
(d) plague is to famine

_____ 6. Vulgar is to courteous as _____.
(a) bankrupt is to hardworking
(b) immature is to educated
(c) irritable is to cheerful
(d) worthwhile is to corrupt

_____ 7. Optimist is to hopeful as _____.
(a) activist is to disruptive
(b) architect is to materialistic
(c) educator is to resolute
(d) villain is to unprincipled

_____ 8. Initial is to final as _____.
(a) assured is to extensive
(b) favorable is to discouraging
(c) gorgeous is to immodest
(d) verbal is to oral

_____ 9. Roadblock is to obstacle as _____.
(a) currency is to rupee
(b) election is to politics
(c) executive is to corporation
(d) grocer is to merchant

_____ 10. Immodest is to conceited as _____.
(a) monotonous is to humdrum
(b) eventual is to successive
(c) significant is to magnified
(d) unreasonable is to fateful

_____ 11. Scheme is to intriguer as _____.
(a) illumination is to light bulb
(b) inquiry is to investigator
(c) nutrition is to glutton
(d) severity is to pessimist

_____ 12. One hundred is to century as _____.
(a) millimeter is to meter
(b) naught is to zero
(c) twelve is to decade
(d) twenty is to score

Lesson 20

Heir to Tradition

Words for Study

heir	competitive	amateur	compensate
precarious	technologist	layman	illumines
plight	sentimental	shoddy	spontaneous

Heir to Tradition

Does the emphasis that so many writers place upon the present mean that we should forget about the past and concentrate on adjusting to the changes taking place around us now? In this excerpt from her book *How to Think About Ourselves*, Bonaro Overstreet presents a thoughtful response to this question.

* * *

"Sometimes I feel like a motherless child..." Thus go the words of the old spiritual, and in them is the haunt of earth's loneliest estate.

If anywhere in our experience there is proof that man does not live by bread alone, it is in the condition of the child left to find its own way in a precarious and confusing world. Relatives, or society at large, may see to it that the orphan does not go cold or hungry, but such elementary care leaves untouched some inner core of loneliness. The lack remains—a lack of a deep sense of belonging.

We recognize the plight of the orphan. Yet many, perhaps most, of us in a deep spiritual sense are voluntary orphans. We have cut ourselves off from the human tradition that is parent to the human present. As a result, there is an uneasiness that cannot be quieted by adding new possessions, by competitive triumphs in our activities, or by joining more organizations. It is the uneasiness of trying to build a new sense of values out of materials that are too flimsy to rely on, of never quite knowing what is important and what does not matter, of trying to go it too much alone, or desperate in aloneness, of running with whatever gang is handy to run with.

Biologists never tire of stressing the fact that man, and only man, is a tradition builder. Birds and beavers can repeat what birds and beavers have done before. But only the human being can begin where others before him have left off. He can do *what they have not done* because he can learn from *what they have done*.

Modern man, confused about his relationship to the past, has built a confused present. Only as a scientist and technologist has he confidently honored the past as it can best be honored by a tradition-building species: *he has learned from it*. He has learned not to repeat its blunders but to carry its triumphs on from stage to stage. In economics, politics, and religion, however, he has consistently dishonored the past. Either he has underestimated his debt to it by pretending to be self-made, or he has refused to budge beyond the stopping point of the past.

Psychiatrists have made it clear that an individual who is consciously or subconsciously at odds with his own past is likely to be an unhappy and sick individual. If he knows nothing at all about his past, he lacks something vital to his sense of completeness. If, on the other hand, he knows his past and resents it, he is again in a bad way. For the expectations and desires that

---

he will bring to present situations and future plans will be so distorted by bitterness that they will cause further distortion. If by contrast he is tied to his past by a sentimental memory of it, he will remain mentally, emotionally, and socially immature. He will be dependent, inclined to cling to the familiar, possessive in friendship and marriage, prone to seek a leader.

Properly speaking, an individual's past is simply the *so-far element* in his life. It contains what he has learned so far, the people he has known so far, the problems he has solved or fumbled so far, the types of behaviors that he has, so far, found reason to condemn or admire. Thus the past is what is supposed to keep an individual from having to be, all his life, a rank amateur in his role as human being. Properly speaking, the past is what a person learns from—and goes on from. The tragedy, as psychiatrists are making us aware, is that the past too often becomes for an individual not something to go from, but something that prevents a healthy going on.

But neither the trained psychiatrist nor the observant layman, it seems to me, has yet paid enough attention to what it does to an individual to have a right or wrong relationship to that shared past we call the human tradition. The pasts that laymen and psychiatrists alike have talked about, in sizing up the behavior of people, have almost always been personal pasts. This man, we say, was once a boy who hated his father and loved his mother. This woman was once a girl who was overshadowed in all that she tried to do by a brilliant and beautiful younger sister.

But what was the relationship of this man or this woman to the longer past, the human past? How were they introduced to it? What were they encouraged to find in it? Has it given them any practical and dependable clues to what is worth wanting and admiring on the human level of life? What habits and attitudes of their own trace back to admiration of what has, throughout history, been proved to have worth?

It seems odd that no psychiatrist has yet—so far as I know—explored the biographical evidence which suggests that many individuals have triumphed over painful and dreary personal pasts because some fortunate accident encouraged them to make the human past their own. In one life story after another we find the theme repeated: that of the lost and lonely child who, through some circumstance, was brought into contact with tradition, was introduced to books through which he learned the difference between what is shoddy in human behavior and what is excellent.

To take one example, we may recall the story that the American writer Langston Hughes tells in his autobiography, *The Big Sea.* A small and lonely son of a despised race, he had the enormous good fortune to discover a public library and in it a librarian who, with a sure sense of the boy's need, introduced him to book after book—gave him the great past as his own; helped him to make it his personal background, so that the standards it set became the standards on which he was ready to stake his life.

Such contact with the past, obviously, is necessary not only to those who are having to compensate for a difficult personal past. For even the most fortunate among us, it is the background that contains more of understanding and compassion, more of courage and dedication, than even the best family background can hold. It both illumines the world in which the individual does his daily living and introduces him to an older and wider world than any he has known.

To say precisely what happens to us when we establish a warm, creative link with the long history of man on earth is as difficult as to say what happens when we experience a great love. We are still the selves we were. Yet we are no longer the selves we were, for we see the world around us so differently that our spontaneous reactions to it are different.

As individuals, we are more than the powers and limitations we were born with. We are, in fact, marked less by these than by our *habits of attention*, the *expectations* we bring to our meetings with life, and the *judgments* we pass upon people and events. Let any new insight change the focus of our attention—so that we notice what we did not notice before—or change our expectations and our habits of judgment, and we may in an instant move mentally and emotionally into a new environment, even though we have not moved from our tracks. Something of this sort is what happens when we fall in love—either with one individual, or with the human race as it speaks for itself through the great tradition.

All through the ages the seers, prophets, saints, artists, and genuine lovers have tried mightily to make the experiences that have transformed them seem real to persons who cannot quite believe them because they have not had matching experiences of their own. When, by word or example, they are able to make it convincing that there is a non-ordinary approach to life which yields a tremendous sense of happiness and freedom, they are able to persuade others—some yearning few—to take a chance on a way of life the worth of which they have not yet tested for themselves.

Among these converts, many will still see so darkly that they will miss the road pointed out to them and stumble, instead, into a path that leads nowhere. Some few, however, will catch on to the fact that what is called for in their lives is a whole new focus of attention, a whole new set of habits and attitudes—ones that will break down the barriers by which they have been held apart from their world and the people in it. They are the few who actually discover the excitement of being human, and strangely enough, at the heart of that excitement, discover the peace that passes understanding.

In a profound sense, the individual who has come to feel his kinship to the human race and his responsible heirship to the human past has gone through such a transforming experience. He probably makes keener distinctions than ever before—for he knows, as never before, what he considers important. But he is no longer alone. He knows himself as a member of the human race.

1 **Understanding the Reading.** Put the letter of the best answer on the line to the left.

_____ 1. Overstreet uses the example of the orphan to illustrate that _____.

(a) nobody chooses to be an orphan
(b) parents often neglect their children
(c) people need more than food, clothing, and shelter
(d) the care received by orphans is better than we often realize

_____ 2. The past, or tradition, in this reading is referred to as a(n) _____.

(a) burden (b) heir (c) orphan (d) parent

_____ 3. *Odds*, as it is used by Overstreet in "Psychiatrists have made it clear that an individual who is at odds with his own past is likely to be an unhappy and sick individual" means _____.

(a) a number of points given to a weaker side in a contest
(b) a ratio expressing the probable outcome of an event
(c) in conflict or disagreement
(d) likelihood

_____ 4. According to the psychiatrists, which word *least* describes a person who is at odds with his past?

(a) dependent (b) incomplete (c) resentful (d) vital

_____ 5. Overstreet's *main* disagreement with the typical view toward the past held by most people is that most of us _____.

(a) blame the past for all our present difficulties
(b) have a sentimental view of the past
(c) emphasize only our personal pasts
(d) spend too much time reliving past events

_____ 6. To explain her disagreement with the typical view of the past, Overstreet uses the example of _____.

(a) Langston Hughes's autobiography
(b) the orphan
(c) the girl who is overshadowed by her younger sister
(d) the "so-far element"

_____ 7. Overstreet contends that _____.

(a) an appreciation of tradition helps everyone who has had a difficult personal past
(b) people can be enriched by an understanding of tradition
(c) tradition is the strongest influence on our present lives
(d) tradition reminds us of how limited we are in our ability to bring about change

2 **Reacting to the Reading.** Answer the following questions in good sentence form.

1. According to Overstreet, many people concentrate on their personal pasts and pay little or no attention to the human past or tradition. What does she feel people can gain from establishing a "warm, creative link with the long history of man on earth"?

2. Do you think that Overstreet is correct in her beliefs? Why or why not?

3. Suppose you decide that Overstreet is right—that "establishing a warm, creative link" with the past is important. How might you go about establishing this link?

3 **A Poem by Langston Hughes.** In the reading selection, Overstreet discusses how the American writer and poet Langston Hughes (1902-1967) made the human past his personal background. Read this poem of his and then answer the questions.

The Negro Speaks of Rivers
by Langston Hughes

I've known rivers:
I've known rivers ancient as the world and older than the flow of human
blood in human veins.

My soul has grown deep like the rivers.

I bathed in the Euphrates when dawns were young.
I built my hut near the Congo and it lulled me to sleep.
I looked upon the Nile and raised the pyramids above it.
I heard the singing of the Mississippi when Abe Lincoln went down
to New Orleans, and I've seen its muddy bosom turn all golden in
the sunset.

I've known rivers:
Ancient, dusky rivers.

My soul has grown deep like the rivers.

---

1. Locate the following using a dictionary or other reference book:

   a. the Euphrates ______________________________

   b. the Congo ______________________________

   c. the Nile ______________________________

   d. New Orleans ______________________________

2. Cite evidence from the poem which shows that Langston Hughes did, as Overstreet stated in the reading, make the human past his personal background.

   ____

   ____

   ____

   ____

3. Why do you think Hughes chose rivers rather than forests or mountains to express his link with the past?

   ____

   ____

   ____

   ____

4. Why do you think Hughes says that his "*soul* has grown deep" rather than his mind or his heart?

   ____

   ____

   ____

   ____

   ____

4 **Synonyms and Antonyms.** Choose a synonym to fill in the first blank in each sentence. Choose an antonym to fill in the second blank.

Synonyms		Antonyms	
ample	leaning	admire	lower
corrupt	obstacle	advantage	stingy
despise	rehabilitate	damage	unemotional
elevate	sentimental	extinguish	unprotected
ignite	shielded	honorable	unwillingness

1. Barrier and ________________ are antonyms for ________________.
2. Generous and ________________ are antonyms for ________________.
3. Kindle and ________________ are antonyms for ________________.
4. Restore and ________________ are antonyms for ________________.
5. Romantic and ________________ are antonyms for ________________.
6. Safe and ________________ are antonyms for ________________.
7. Scorn and ________________ are antonyms for ________________.
8. Tendency and ________________ are antonyms for ________________.
9. Unprincipled and ________________ are antonyms for ________________.
10. Uplift and ________________ are antonyms for ________________.

5 **Spelling Check.** One tradition with which we are familiar is Thanksgiving. In each of these items about the celebration of Thanksgiving, one of the underlined words may be misspelled. Write that word, spelled correctly, on the line. If none of the words is misspelled, write *all right* on the line.

_______________ 1. Although a day reserved for general thanksgiving—especially at harvest time—has been observed by almost every nation in almost every historacal period, Thanksgiving Day as observed in the United States has evolved as a unique American feast.

_______________ 2. Probably the first thanksgiving service in America, which was held on May 27, 1578, by the members of an expidition that had landed on the shores of Newfoundland, was conducted by an English minister who preached a thanksgiving sermon.

_______________ 3. Those, however, were merely thanksgiving services, and the origin of a *day* of thanksgiving such as we now celabrate must be granted to Governor Bradford of Plymouth.

_______________ 4. After landing on the desolate coast of New England in November 1620, the Pilgrums passed the winter with great suffering and watched the growth of the seed they planted in spring with great anxiety. For on the result depended the lives of the colonists.

_______________ 5. When the grain was cut and the harvest was found to be abundant, there was great rejoicing and the governor proclaimed a day of thanksgiving. He sent out four men in search of game, and they soon returned with a large number of wild foul, most of which were turkeys.

_______________ 6. Incidentally, one etymologist tells the doubtful but amusing story of how the turkey is said to have gotten its name from the doctor on Columbus's first voyage who exclaimed "Tukki!" (the Hebrew word for "big bird") on seeing this unusual specimen for the first time.

_______________ 7. The first Thanksgiving feast probably consisted of turkeys, ducks, geese, native squash and pumpkin. The provisions must have been abundant, for about one hundred fourty persons, including ninety Indians, were entertained for three days.

_______________ 8. The specific date of this festival is not known, but acording to records it must have occurred between September 23rd and November 11th in 1621.

_______________ 9. On October 3, 1789, George Washington issued a proclamation appointing Thursday, November 26, 1789, as a day of general thanksgiving, and this day may be considered the first national Thanksgiving Day.

_______________ 10. Thanksgiving days were irregularly celebrated after this and almost never in the South; but in 1864, President Lincoln issued a proclamation appointing the forth Thursday in November as Thanksgiving Day, with a view of having the day observed every year thereafter.

______ 11. The adoption of the last Thursday in November as a uniform date for observence of Thanksgiving was largely due to the efforts of Mrs. Sarah J. Hale, a well-known author and editor of the late nineteenth century.

______ 12. Although Thanksgiving Day is still observed by feasting and general festivity, the electronic era of television has resulted in millions of Americans being thankfull for the broadcast of football games rather than for the abundance of nature that brought about Thanksgiving Day in the first place.

Review: Lessons 1 - 20

1 **Definitions.** Match the words listed below with the correct definitions.

canopy	infirmity	palpitation	savvy
decade	interval	plight	shoddy
famine	minority	potential	technology
flux	obstacle	precarious	unabridged

_______________ 1. a covering hung over a throne, bed, or entrance

_______________ 2. a difficult condition or situation

_______________ 3. a continued flow or flood

_______________ 4. a drastic and wide-reaching shortage of food; severe hunger

_______________ 5. a period of ten years

_______________ 6. inferior; of poor quality

_______________ 7. a trembling or shaking; irregular or rapid beating of the heart

_______________ 8. not condensed; complete

_______________ 9. any weakness or illness

_______________ 10. something that stands in the way or interferes

_______________ 11. risky and uncertain; dangerous, hazardous

_______________ 12. practical understanding or knowledge; common sense (slang)

_______________ 13. the inner ability or capacity for growth or development

_______________ 14. the application of scientific and industrial skills to practical uses

_______________ 15. a distance or space between two objects or points; the time between two events

_______________ 16. a group of people different in some way from the larger group of which it is a part

2 **Vocabulary Review.** Write the letter of the best answer on the line to the left.

_____ 1. A jeweler would most likely describe a(n) _____ as artificial.
(a) amethyst (b) rhinestone (c) sapphire (d) topaz

_____ 2. The abbreviation _____ is *not* commonly part of a business's name.
(a) Co. (b) Corp. (c) A.D. (d) Inc.

_____ 3. A(n) _____ frequently uses a kiln.
(a) architect (b) carpenter (c) chef (d) potter

_____ 4. A person watching a sentimental movie might request a(n) _____.
(a) handkerchief (b) intermission (c) snack (d) usher

_____ 5. A sociologist would probably *not* spend a lot of time studying _____.
(a) battleships (b) courtships (c) friendships (d) kinships

_____ 6. Amateurs are generally _____.
(a) unfriendly (b) unhealthy (c) unmarried (d) unpaid

_____ 7. A person prone to spontaneous actions is rarely _____.
(a) conscious (b) self-conscious (c) subconscious (d) unconscious

_____ 8. The *hearth* is frequently used to symbolize _____ life.
(a) domestic (b) international (c) patriotic (d) tropical

3 **Vocabulary Review.** Match the words listed at the left with what they best describe.

abridged
competitive
desolate
economical
offensive
portable
reliable
sentimental

_______________ 1. a 20,000 word dictionary

_______________ 2. a small television set

_______________ 3. a professional tennis player

_______________ 4. a scrapbook lover

_______________ 5. a thrifty householder

_______________ 6. a trustworthy employee

_______________ 7. an empty landscape

_______________ 8. a vulgar insult

4 **Growth and Change.** The chart below records the population in five different periods of American history. Refer to both the chart and a dictionary, if necessary, to answer the questions.

Population Growth and Change

Year	Total population	Rural	Urban
1607	about 100	100%	
1753	1,328,000	98%	2%
1850	23,191,876	85%	15%
1869	38,925,000	75%	25%
1917	101,297,851	50%	50%
1929	121,670,000	44%	56%
1930	122,775,046	44%	56%
1959	175,608,490	31%	69%
1960	179,323,175	30%	70%
1987	242,600,000	26%	74%

1. Define the word *rural.* ______________________

2. Define the word *urban.* ______________________

3. In which year was three-fourths of the population classified as rural? ______________________

4. During which war did the rural population equal the urban population: the Civil War, World War I, or World War II? ______________________

5. In what year does the figure recorded for the urban population first exceed the rural population figure? ______________________

6. Which period marks the greatest shift in population from rural to urban: 1917-1929, 1930-1959, or 1960-1987? ______________________

7. Which period marks the greatest increase in population: 1917-1929, 1930-1959, or 1960-1987? ______________________

8. How many more people were recorded in the 1987 population figure than in 1607?

____

5 **Time and Change.** The puzzle below contains a message that Roy Campanella would probably agree with. When the clues are completed correctly, the initial letters of the words, reading downward, spell a word that is a synonym for *change*. Refer to Exercise 5 of the Review of Lessons 1-10 if you have forgotten how to do this type of puzzle.

Blanks	Clue
__ __ __ __ __ __ 36 15 65 72 2 51	1. Another word for seesaw: _____-totter
__ __ __ __ __ __ __ 26 76 43 29 44 35 7	2. A weed which causes hay fever
__ __ __ __ __ __ __ 39 11 34 17 66 47 55	3. A drug widely used for headaches
__ __ __ __ 19 67 49 31	4. Scolds or pesters
__ __ __ __ __ 68 64 58 23 46	5. To fire a gun
__ __ __ __ __ 50 21 8 3 63	6. A special meal; a celebration
__ __ __ __ __ __ 28 40 71 59 74 16	7. A source of pearls
__ __ __ __ __ __ 6 12 53 70 38 9	8. A relief or cure
__ __ __ __ __ __ 24 62 38 5 42 57	9. Not boastful; humble
__ __ __ __ __ __ __ 8 77 13 30 61 22 1	10. An uneasy, worried feeling
__ __ __ __ __ __ __ 45 40 14 60 37 25 77	11. What a hurricane in the China Sea is called
__ __ __ __ 10 33 73 39	12. Des Moines is the capital of this Midwestern state
__ __ __ __ __ __ __ 52 75 4 54 69 18 27	13. The month in which Halloween occurs
__ __ __ __ __ 48 41 20 32 56	14. The area within a habitat occupied by an organism

_ _ _ _ _ _ _ _ _   _ _   _ _ _ _ _ _ _ _ _ _.
1 2 3 4 5 6 7 8 9   10 11   12 13 14 15 16 17 18 19 20 21

_ _ _ _ _ _ _ _   _ _   _ _ _ _.   _ _ _ _ _
22 23 24 25 26 27 28 29   30 31   32 33 34 35   36 37 38 39 40

_ _   _ _ _ _ _ _ _   _ _ _ _   _ _ _   _ _
41 42   43 44 45 46 47 48 49   50 51 52 53   54 55 56   57 58

_ _ _   _ _ _ _ _   _ _   _ _ _ _   _ _   _ _ _.
59 60 61   62 63 64 65 66   67 68   69 70 71 72   73 74   75 76 77

The synonym for *change*: _ _ _ _ _ _ _ _ _ _ _ _ _ _